She's Just Like Me

Never Send a Man to do a Woman's Job

Published by: Boss Status Publishing

304 S. Jones Blvd

Suite 2222

Las Vegas, NV 89107

Books published by Boss Status Publishing are available at exclusive discounts for bulk purchase by corporations, institutions, individuals and other organizations.

Edited by: Sherice Sr.

Cover design: Mario Patterson

Models: Gary Jones and Angel Moore

Photo: Mark Gatson Photography

ISBN 978-0-9969407-4-0

Printed in the United States of America

Dedication

This book is dedicated to my dearest mother, Catherine Tate. I learned much of my "Love, and Respect" watching you live out yours for others and myself. When no one else believed in me, you always had my back. You are my best friend that raised three wonderful children: Greg, Charleszette, and myself. I love you with all my heart. I am honored to be your daughter. Rest in Heaven Greg.

Contents

Acknowledgments

I give all praise to my Lord and Savior, Jesus Christ. With Him, all things are possible. He has given me a gift to do something positive with my life without damaging consequences for my actions. He is my rock. To my mother and stepfather, Catherine and John Tate: You guys are fantastic and positive role models in my life. When I first started writing, even though I didn't know what I was doing, you guys said to go for it. And now I've been blessed to write several books. Thank you for the support and believing in my dream. To my father, Charles Harrison: I thank you very much for having my back and always being in my life the way a Father is supposed to be. You and mom have always been here for me, even in the toughest time of my life. During My four-and-a-half-year prison sentence, you guys never judged me but told me to trust God and to keep my faith. To the three loves of my life, my children, Benjamin, Shamika, and Sharoni'a I love you guys dearly. To my seven Grandchildren, Ziah, Bryana, Neveah, Khaaliq, Akeem Jr, Khloe, and Royal: I have unconditional love for you all, always and forever.

To my BFF/Business partner, Sherice Sr., thanks for the support while I revised this book, to release it under our Boss Status Publishing company. It's all gas, no brakes. To my family and friends that gave me ideas and worked on this book with me, during the wee hours of the night, writing and typing, even though I didn't have a clue what I was doing, still, you guys believed in me. I thank you. Shamika, you're always down with whatever mommy does. Megan Jackson, who is no longer with me (RIH): I miss you so much little sister, you are greatly appreciated and missed. Shout out to my two sisters in Omaha, Nebraska, Dorothy and Reenita: I love you ladies and your children. Blessings to my crew, you girls, always had my back, regardless of any situation. We were off the chain but stood strong. Mary Kay, Charleszette, Melanie, Victoria, Tracy, Devon, Bonnie, Rita, Tona, and Denise, Latoya, Mika, Dashan, and Renee. Super shout out to my brothers and guy friends, Chad, Dale, Cortez, Vaughn, John, Brian, Lamont, Stephon, Rasheed, Ramon, J. Diggs. You guys had an impact on my life in some form or another, thanks for life lessons. Shout out to my neighbor Allison, for always helping me along the way with my books. Finally, my publishing company, Boss Status Publishing and Team BSP, for your dedication to helping our business get off the ground, "Alicia Boo Mills," Krealonna, RIP my lovely niece, you're out of sight, but never out of mind. I appreciate you more than you could ever know. Anthony and Ben, much love!

To everyone around the world in the prison system and maybe doing more time than you deserve, I know what you're going through. I have so much empathy for you all.

Whatever higher power you serve or believe, just know you will see better days. Keep your faith.

Introduction

It was a beautiful, hot, cloudless, sunny June day. My birthday party had already started, and we were kicking it hard. Usually, I would celebrate my birthday with my daughter Angel because our birthdays were only a day apart. We weren't this year. There wouldn't be any children around, just the grown and sexy, except a few hood rats and a couple of shit-starting men that acted like boys. Shelter number seven in Swope Park, today would make history. We were ready to party like rock stars. Everyone was showing up. All the D-boys were pulling up in their best whips, and most cars were sitting on Dayton's and vogues, with candy paint to accommodate the rides. If I do say so myself, they were showing off. It was a party mixed with a car show.

For it to be Kansas City, Missouri, the party was turning out exceptionally well. All the hot girls came out knowing all the cats that were about something or had money would be there. I had Cush all bagged up. Hundred-dollar sacks, seven grams to Ounces, ready to sell. If they wanted more, my partner Mac was on his way, knowing that I would run out of weed fast. Today would be a day to remember.

Mac had pulled up with his boys, most of which I knew, and some new cats from Cali that I hadn't met before. They were all beautiful as hell and looked like they worked out seven days a week. That made me assume that they had likely done prison time. Tracy and I were checking them out as they walked our way, and the first thing that came to my mind was that there would most definitely be some choosing up today, I always made sure that I would choose to win. Of course, not before getting a background check on them from Mac, and seeing what they were about, like if they were the help or the hope. I knew California men wined and dined their women, smoked the best weed, and ate the best pussy in the U.S. shit, the world in my eyes! The cons? If you didn't know the game, they would put you to work fast in some shape, form, or fashion. From selling dope, driving their drugs or money to different destinations, or putting a car or a house in your name, shit even make you sell that thang for some change, only if you fell for the slick talk. Some of the cats were some slick talkers, wanna be pimps! Thank goodness that I wasn't anyone's flunky or mule. It was hard to sell me a dream, and I played by my own rules.

Mac introduced us to his friends, and once they saw the money that was hanging off my shirt, they started taking fat bankrolls out of their pockets, pinning fifties and hundreds on me. The money was coming fast, and I loved every bit of it. The crap game going on was where all the big money cats were. There had to be no less than ten thousand down on the concrete. With chronic smoke blowing all around, the scene looked like a hip-hop video. After Mac had introduced us and the money was exchanged, they headed straight over to see what was going on. Big Ike was running the game. His daughter and I weren't very fond of one another because she was messing with my sister Charlie's husband. That didn't stop Big Ike and me from being friends. He was a cool OG that I respected. Plus, he was passionate about the crap games and won a lot of money doing it. Craps could have been his real job, had it been legal on the streets. He called the shots, he was the houseman all around town, and today he would take home a few thousand no matter what. Mac and his boys joined the crap game. Someone was going to come up with some big money or leave short as a dwarf because they weren't playing with small bills.

My girls Tracy, Charlie, Vickie, Tabby, and Trecie, were serving tropical fruit out of gutted watermelons, and we were all wearing hula dresses. The theme of the party was the tropical islands of Hawaii. They welcomed everyone who showed up with a blunt in his or her mouth. The women were greeted with skirts, the men with a lei flower necklace. Our whole click was looking sexy, as usual. All the men, and most women, the ones that wasn't hating on one or all of us, respected my crew. Everything was perfect in my eyes. I felt like a queen. I was the queen. That's the name that my homeboy gave me when I started selling drugs, so it stuck! And boy did I live up to it. I bought the whole city out to Swope Park. Well, the state. If no one else could bring them out, I could. I even had cats show up from St. Louis and California was definitely in attendance. Since Kansas City, Kansas, was right across the bridge, all my people showed up in packs from over there. The music was being played from one of the trucks, and it sounded like a club because the turntables needed a special adapter. After Tracy and J.C. had grabbed the part for the turntables that D.J. Les needed to play the music, it was on. D.J. Les was rocking that shit like he always did when he D.J. a party! He played some east coast music, but, E.40, Tupac, and Mac Dre were Kansas City's favorites, so that's what he played most, and of course Kansas City's celebrity, Rich the Factor, which made the party hype. I was ready to smoke a few ounces of Cush and get my party on. I was smiling and welcoming everyone to my birthday luau, trying to make everyone comfortable, and be cordial. Chicks that didn't like my crew or me were showing up by the carloads. Shit, if you can't beat them, join them. That was my motto, and that's precisely what they were doing. It was the party of the year, and if you weren't in formation, then you were nobody.

There was so much liquor, cases, kegs of beer and everyone was having a wonderful time. There were three cats there that liked me so I was feeling like a player and they probably were feeling the same, like they were the men that I chose to be there with me, not knowing that I was kicking it with all three of them on the low. L walked over to each one of them and told them what I was going to do to them once the party was over, but truly I was only sleeping with the chosen one. I played hard, just like the cats that I dealt with, even harder than a couple. I was just like them, a female baller, feminine gangster. Some would call it hoeing; I called it getting what I wanted when I wanted it. Maybe it was an attempt to make it sound better, but there were levels, and I felt I was on a higher standard than others that never got anything from a man. I was the queen of my city.

There was so much food that we could have fed everyone at both city missions. Charlie came and pinned a few more twenties and fifties on me; the money train was awesome! I knew by the end of the day that I would have at least a few thousand dollars and if the night went well, maybe five thousand. The twenties, fifties, and hundreds were coming. Not everyone has to sell ass to get cash. As much liquor as I had, people were still bringing fifths of Remy Martin, Hennessy, Vodka, and cases of beer. The leftover liquor would go home with me for sure. We were going to party non-stop. My birthday would last the whole month of June because that's how I celebrated it every year.

Everyone was laughing at Bug and J.C. on the ugly ass scooter, moped, or whatever it was that he had driven to the party. Bug was a big girl to be riding on such a small, weird-looking machine. If you asked me, it looked like someone may have thrown it together from junk pieces before J.C. got to the picnic. However, he had wheels and rode all the way from 35th and Chestnut to the park on 63rd Street. Everyone's focus was on them. That was the laugh of the day, Black ass J.C. and Big Bug bouncing down the street on a miniature moped.

More and more people were showing up, and as a result, I was running around and talking so that everyone would feel comfortable and welcomed. Suddenly everyone started running and screaming. At the parties I go to, I know that when people start running, more than likely, there's trouble. There were a few troublemakers there, and we all know what we do when things like that happen. We run! So, I ran. I didn't understand why they were running, but when black people see other people running, it is usually about to be some bullshit. The next thing I heard was Pow! POW! Pow! POW! I hit the ground next to the car that I was running past and laid there for a few minutes, scared to get up and see what was going on. My heart was beating so fast; I thought it was coming out of my chest. It was all I could hear. My knee was bleeding from diving to the ground. I knew that it had to be something that had gone wrong with that crap game because of all that money that had been on the ground. Maybe it was a robbery or someone cheating in the game. I thought, "Was someone robbing everybody?" Shit, all kinds of thoughts were going through my mind. I was praying that no one was shot. Once the shooting stopped, I got up, peeped around the car to make sure everything was cool, then I ran up the hill to see what went down. Vickie was kneeling down, holding him, rubbing his head and telling him not to die and that everything was going to be alright. Out of everyone why him and why at my party?

CHAPTER 1
WHAT A CREATION: A GOOD GIRL'S LIFE

I was born in Omaha, Nebraska. As a young child who grew up in the 70's, my mother and father made sure that my siblings, and I had a good home. My brother Isiah was the oldest, my sister Charlie was the middle child, and I was the youngest. They were six and seven years older than me. My mother said she was finished having kids after them, but somehow, I popped up. She used to tell me, "You snuck up on me, but now that you're here, I love you." I was overjoyed when she said that because I felt special that she allowed me to make it into this world.

My siblings and I truly adored our parents very much; we had a great loving family. We also stayed in the church. We attended service on Sundays, bible study on Wednesday nights, choir rehearsal on Thursday nights, and if there were services on Fridays, we attended those. We were Pentecostal, and we had a live congregation. My uncle was the pastor of the church, and he could preach. Everyone would be shouting, feeling good in the spirit. I would beat the tambourine and praise the Lord right with them. I would love to see my mom and aunt get in the spirit. They had their dance, and they would cut it up.

I remember sometimes I would bring my best friend, Abby, to church with me. She was white, and her family was a different religion, she had never seen anyone shout before. She would laugh and ask me what was going on and what they were doing. I would tell her that they were happy and that's how we gave thanks to God. People would be speaking in tongues. I can even recall on a few occasions when my uncle would cast out demons. People said that it was crazy, but I knew that it was real because I watched it happen. My uncle would get the blessed oil, and the prayer warriors would all start praying over the possessed person. They would fall to the ground and start foaming at the mouth. That's when they said that the demon was coming out. We would have to hold our Bibles up and pray also; they said that would stop the demons from jumping into us. I was never scared because I had seen it performed so many times before. But the whole thing was crazy as hell. It was like watching the movie, "The Exorcist." Their eyes would roll to the back of their heads, and after a few minutes of praying, the demons would be cast out. The person would get up, and you could see a change in them like a weight had been lifted off their shoulders. That was some wild shit. My mom, Charlie, and I were in the choir. My mom would sing lead on most of the songs because she could sing, no she could blow, like Shirley Caesar. Charlie and I led a couple of songs, too. We couldn't blow like momma and her sisters, but we could hold a note. She was always teaching us how to harmonize. We had deep alto voices. People would ask us all the time if we were hoarse or if we had a cold. We just had deep, raspy sounds that came from my father's side of the family; maybe momma's as well.

My brother Isiah played the drums and the organ for the choir. He was good at it too. My dad never went to church, but he had every gospel album that was out. There were 33 altogether. His favorites were the Gospel Keynotes, the William Brothers, and the Five Blind Boys. Every Sunday morning before we headed out to the church he would pull out his collection and play music. I would sit next to him in his lazy boy chair and sing my heart out. He would say, "Dee" (that's what he called me), "you show can sing girl." I would smile and tell him he should come to church and hear me. My dad would always say that he would, but he never did. I didn't care because I was used to him not coming to church. All that mattered to me was that he was a great father and I knew that he would be home when we returned.

As a young girl, I always knew that life would be filled with ups and downs. My parents were well established. Both were employed with great jobs. My father was a truck driver, and my mom was a laboratory technician at the hospital. They both made nice salaries, and thus, they could quickly move out of the low-income projects. By the time I was born, they had moved to a lovely house. We had white furniture, in the front room where we were not allowed. We had a bar and pool table amongst other things in our basement. My brother, Isiah had his room down there. Charlie and I shared a bedroom, and the guest bedroom was next to ours, with momma and daddy in the master bedroom.

In 1975, I remembered my parents owning a brand new Cadillac from off the showroom floor. I loved smelling the fresh new leather seats in our cars. After a few years of having the cars, they would upgrade for more modern modes.

My dad also had a motorcycle and attended the Zodiacs MC club. He was super cool with his brothers in the club. They were like our extended family. I loved to go to the club because they would give me dollar bills. I was obsessed with money, and as soon as I got it, I would go to the corner store to buy candy.

I remember thinking, "this is the lifestyle that I have, and always want to keep." I would tell my friends that I was going to grow up and be just like my mom: Married, in church, drug-free, smart with a great job. She was a super mom. She did what she could to prepare us for the world and the life ahead of us.

Another love of mine that started early was cooking. My mom taught me how to cook at a very young age. When she had to work late, she would tell me to cook dinner and gave me directions to prepare the food. I loved to cook. I never burned food because no matter how long it took to cook I would sit in the kitchen and wait for it to get done. I would do my homework and wait for the chicken to bake. Cooking also made me focus better on my studies. I couldn't go outside if I was cooking, so homework made the cooking process go by faster. I was the youngest child and could out-cook both of my older siblings. Not only them, but I could also cook better than a lot of grown folks, and it became one of my passions. Momma would get off work and taste the food, saying "Dee, you seasoned that meat like a grown woman. You put your foot in that food; you go, girl." It made me feel ecstatic. I would smile while everyone was eating up my food thinking that one day I would be in the restaurant business and my food would be great!

I also liked riding around with my parents. No matter where they went, I jumped in the car. No matter how far we went, I knew my way back. I paid close attention to everywhere we went. I would sit and look out the window and remember every place that I was going. Landmarks, buildings, shortcuts, the long way, I memorized them all. When family or friends would come into town, and no one wanted to drive them around, my mom would tell them that I knew how to get anywhere they wanted to go. I would show everyone how to get around. I would become their tour guide, and they would pay me for my time and services.

I was a human navigation system. They would say things like, "You are so young, how did you learn to get around like this?" I would tell them that no matter what car I was in that, I would watch and observe streets and landmarks. This started another passion for me. Traveling! I was obsessed with traveling. My family and I would visit Texas and Missouri. My dad's family lived in a small town in Texas called Linden. It was tiny with a population of two thousand, if not less, and most of the people in the city were our family.

There wasn't much to do in the town, but we always had a great time amongst each other. My grandmother, affectionately known as MawMaw, would cook the best breakfast in the world. I had never had a fresh egg from a chicken. The eggs were so yellow that I would be scared to eat them. My grandfather, who I called PaPa, had a farm with animals in the back yard. It may not have been a farm, but they had a lot of land, the eggs came right from the chickens, and the meat came from the pigs. The butcher at the market would cut the meat .and pack it for them. We would eat all day while we were there. MawMaw cooked everything, and when she didn't cook, my uncle Boots, who lived not too far from her, would have food ready all at his expense since he owned a restaurant.

My dad's mom could cook and my mom's mother could cook also. I had it good on both sides of my family. For fun, while we were in Texas, my siblings, cousins, and I would beat on the pigs in the pen. It sounded crazy, and now I know that it was animal cruelty, but it was fun! The pigs would run from corner to corner squealing! We would hit them with whips, not knowing we were hurting them. I always had a ball in the country, because it was calm and our family all lived close which made it easy to see everyone. But I never wanted to live there, only visit. I was a city girl and I enjoyed the city life. Before we would head back to Omaha, we always stopped in Dallas. Dad would take us to Six Flags over Texas and we would have a ball.

I would never ride the Ferris wheels or roller coasters, but I still loved the amusement park. Six Flags was huge, unlike Peony Park. That was our amusement park back in Omaha. There was no comparison. Isiah would ride everything he could, but Charlie and I only rode water rides and bumper cars. When we left the park, we would always stop at a particular restaurant before we got back on the road.

I don't remember the name of the restaurant, but they had the biggest burgers that I had ever seen. The burger was called "Texas Giant." It was so big that Charlie and I had to split one. Isiah always ate a whole one by himself. A half was like eating a Burger King Whopper. Daddy would still order a T-bone steak. Steaks were his favorite, especially momma's. Theirs had to be good also because he never got anything different. Momma got chicken and I ate off both of their plates. The food was great. When we finished eating we got back on the road and headed back home to Omaha.

I would watch the freeways leaving Texas and know which way to get back home. 35 North, I always paid attention. We always stopped in

Kansas City before we got back to Omaha. My mother's oldest sister lived there. We went to K.C. as often as we could to visit her; it was three hours from Omaha. We stayed on the go. I was ready to go out of town all the time because that meant all new clothes. Momma would get us new clothes to take on the trips, and even though we already had plenty of clothes, vacations meant more. My mother would keep my siblings and me looking nice. Because of my mother's expensive taste, I looked down on anything other than the best. For instance, even though momma shopped at garage sales, they were not my scene. But my mother and sister loved them. We would pull up to a yard sale, and I wouldn't budge. My mom would hit me, saying that I was no better than anyone else and if I didn't get out and try something on, that when I got home she would tear my butt up. It was crazy to me that she had a passion for yard sales. Just the thought of wearing strangers' clothes made me itch and sick to my stomach. Even though they were taken home and washed, they were still some strangers' clothing. I realized that I had expensive taste and my love for clothes made me different.

Once I was twelve, I started paying more attention to things. A few months went by and I noticed that my father stopped coming to dinner with us as often as he did. He would show up now and then, but things seemed to be a little off. I would ask momma where daddy was. She would always say that he was working late or that he had a late poker game. Daddy played poker a lot but never this much, not to the point of missing dinner. I also observed momma's patterns; She wasn't cooking daddy's meals like she usually did. Usually, she would cook us spaghetti and salad, and dad would get a steak, fried potatoes, and veggies, but none of this was being prepared. He was eating the same thing that we ate. He was still coming home but something just wasn't right.

Momma started working more and more hours. I was back to cooking dinner and cleaning the kitchen. I was a good cook, but I was missing momma's meals. She usually cooked every day, and now it only three or four times a week. This was still good because I would go to my friends' houses and their moms never cooked, nor did they ever have dinner together. They only ate Swanson's TV dinners or sandwiches, so I was blessed for those meals that we did receive. We got great home-cooked meals, and even if I had to cook them, we were eating well.

Daddy had started getting home so late that I wouldn't see him until I woke up in the morning to get ready for school. I was used to sitting with him in the evenings in his recliner, watching TV. Now it wasn't happening. Once, I asked him why he was working so much. He replied that he needed extra cash so that he could take care of all the bills that we had. I knew we had bills, but it never stopped him from being home on time before. I told him that I understood. Besides, he spoiled my siblings and me, and I didn't want that to stop. Life went on. I couldn't wait for the weekends to come. Charlie and I would get to go to Grandma's and play with our cousins. Grandma made the best-smothered chicken and homemade biscuits every morning. I loved to watch her cook, and she made the best homemade caramel cake that I'd ever tasted in my entire life. It melted in your mouth. Grandma would let all the kids stay the night, and we would have a ball with each other.

When Sunday came, we would load up and head to church with her. I don't think my grandmother could drive because one of my aunties or someone from Grandma's church always picked us up. Grandmas church powerhouse was real strict; we knew better than to run our mouths or try to chew gum because you just might get embarrassed if you were caught.

One thing was for sure, as young as I was I listened and always paid attention to the pastor. His word meant something to me. That's where loyalty and trust came in, and no matter what, I would always put God first, and everything after would fall in line.

After church, my mother, aunts, and uncles would meet at Grandma's. We ate dinner together, a family tradition. My cousins and I would play around the house while the grownups would talk, laugh, and sing the day away, having everyone feeling overjoyed. Then everyone would go their separate ways.

I always got home from school before Charlie and Isiah. I would sit at home and watch good times when the phone would ring. I would answer, only to get hung up on, which made me nervous. I remembered a few weeks back when I answered the phone and the same thing happened. I was home alone and scared. I called momma and told her what happened and asked her if I could go to the neighbors until Charlie and Isiah came home. We never got hang-ups, and now that it was happening, it was spooky.

One day momma got off early and was cooking dinner when the phone rang. Momma answered the phone. She looked puzzled. Momma said that she was going to her room to take the call and to hang it up when she got to the other phone. Before I hung up, I listened for a minute, like nosey kids did when we had landlines. It was a woman's voice that I had never heard before. I hung up, wondering what the call was about and why my mom wouldn't talk in front of me like she usually did. She never left the room to speak, not even when the bill collectors called. She talked right in our face, but not today, and she looked distraught. I was so proud of my mom and never wanted to see her hurt. She was and still is my pride and joy. I knew when something was wrong with her. I felt her pain just like she always felt mine. We loved daddy dearly, but we were momma's babies.

I would soon find out what the call was about. My father had been cheating on momma, and not with one woman, but with two.

Chapter 2
The Transformation

As a teenager, some things changed. Momma found out about daddy cheating. This quickly ended in a separation, then divorce. Momma already knew about the women, but she wanted us to stay out of it, so she didn't tell us. My father had always been with momma but like most men had other women on the side. None met the pedigree of my mother. I'm not saying that because she was my mom, but because of what I saw with my own eyes. Regardless of the divorce, I still adored my father. He continued to take care of us. We received more out of him then when he was in the house. I guess he felt guilty for doing momma wrong and abandoning his family.

Daddy moved out and went to live with one of his girlfriends. It was so crazy because he left us to go live with a woman who had four young kids and lived in the projects. She had no job and only welfare to live on. We got away from the project lifestyle several years before this, and here he was going backward, moving right back there. Momma didn't appear very hurt because she laughed about it, although I'm sure she was. Twenty-two years is a long time to be with someone and throw everything you have together away. Had it had been a woman who she felt was up to her standards, it may have hurt her more, but she quickly got over him and moved on with her life.

With all the chaos that was going on, I continued to be a good daughter. My best friend and I always hung around the house. We dressed alike, went to school, and kept our grades up. I started playing volleyball and basketball. We were not into boys, just clothes, school, and sports. I was very athletic and smart. My mother was strict and she kept a watchful eye on me. The only place I could go was to my cousin's house, and my friend's houses were out of the question. When I was with my best friend Tia, we did everything that we could before we had to go home. We would walk to Fontanelle Park after school and sit around and talk or walk across the street to A&W to get something to eat. We would talk while we sat and drank root beer floats and ate a couple of ten cent butter biscuits. They were so good that they would melt in your mouth. After we finished our floats we would head back to the park. There were always a lot of boys playing basketball there, and even though we were both still virgins, we liked to look at the boys.

Some of them would try to talk to us, but we weren't interested. We would laugh and keep walking. We did have a crush on a couple of boys but they didn't know. Tia had a crush on my favorite boy cousin June, and I had a crush on Kendal. The girls liked my cousin June. He was fine and he could sing his butt off. He always made me cry when he sang. He sang in a gospel group. I sang with them sometimes but I couldn't sing like June. I don't know if June was still a virgin, but Tia and I were and we said that we wouldn't sleep with a man until we were married. That would change quickly.

One day we walked to the park and Tia met a cute boy named Mike that she liked, and they started going out. Tia talked with him on the phone all night until they fell asleep. He took all my talk time up because I didn't get to stay at her house, which made me jealous of their relationship. I knew this was how life was going to be. After all, we were teenagers and that's what teens do. One day after school, Tia told me that she wanted me to go to the park with her because her boyfriend Mike wanted me to meet his older brother Willie. I thought, "An older brother? He'll be too old for me." Tia said that he was only three years older. Plus, he was high yellow, bow legged, and cute, so I agreed, and we headed to the park.

When we got to the park, Mike and his brother Willie were playing basketball. Willie was cute, light-skinned and bow legged, just like she described. In the 80's, light-skinned men were the bomb. And if they had light eyes, they had all the girls. I told Tia that I thought he was cute and she introduced us. I was shy but cheesin' real hard.

Willie and I started talking on the phone for hours every day. He was older and the way he spoke was very mature. He made me feel wanted, and the more he talked the big boy stuff, the more I was into him. We had better conversations than the young boys I usually spoke to. He asked me to go out with him after a few weeks. I had a boyfriend an older one. We met in the park every day. We would sit and tongue kiss for hours until we had to go home. Tia and I were so close and we were glad that we had hooked up with brothers.

She dated the younger brother and me the eldest. After a few more weeks of hanging together, Willie told me that he loved me. No boy had ever said to me that they loved me. He had my head up in the clouds. I was so happy, and I told him that I loved him back. I thought that I was in love, but it was more along the lines of puppy lust. Tia and I would go over to the brothers' house. Willie would always want to kiss and grind. Once he had mastered first and second base, he started putting his fingers down my pants to finger me. I didn't like it at first and stayed dry, but after he had done it several times, told me to relax and started kissing on my neck, I let go. It felt so good, but I told him that I wasn't ready to have sex. He knew that I was a virgin and said that he wanted to be the first man inside of me. He told me that he was going to marry me, and talked how we would have children and move away from Omaha. He told me everything that a young lady, or rather a kid, wanted to hear.

Willie wasn't a virgin by far. He told me how women kept trying to give him sex and how he was trying to hold out and wait for me. He told me that since I was his girlfriend I needed to have sex with him before he had sex with someone else. What I didn't know was that he was already having sex with other girls and selling me a dream. I was young and had never been pressured to sleep with anyone, and I was in no rush. Willie didn't want to hear any more excuses from me and told me that he was tired of waiting. He told me that he was breaking up with me. He said kissing and grinding were for kids and he was a man. He wanted a woman who would satisfy his sexual appetite. He told me to fuck off and find a little boy to play with because I was a little girl and he wanted a woman. I was in lust and wanted him to remain, my boyfriend, I agreed giving up my virginity to him. At that moment, my innocence went "out the window." My friend Abby was so upset when I told her. She was the only person besides Tia who I could talk to about the situation. I was even afraid to tell Charlie; she would have listened and told me what was right.

Abby and I had been friends since we were five years old. She was a white girl who always had good advice. Abby was smart, she loved my family and me, and the feeling was mutual. Her mother was my mother's attorney. I told her what I did and she said to me that I better hope I wasn't pregnant and that I should have waited. I knew she was right but I had felt pressured.

Willie's penis was huge. He didn't care that I was a virgin. He wasn't the least bit gentle ramming his dick inside of me. So, his friends and brother wouldn't hear me hollering from the other room, he put his tongue in my mouth, damn near down my throat, and pushed his big, man-sized penis inside of me, whispering in my ear, shut up, breath, and relax. I tried to relax he was hurting me. After we had sex, I stopped answering Willie's calls because I was so embarrassed. I had bled all over the sheets, and I yelled for him to stop because he went inside of me so hard, pounding, and I knew that all the guys heard me and were probably laughing at me. To make matters worse, I had to walk home, more than five miles, with my jacket covering my yellow, blood-stained pants. It was a horrible day that I wish never happened. I was too young and most certainly not ready. I told Abby and Tia that I would never sleep with another boy again, or at least that's what I thought.

At that point in our lives, Tia, Abby, and I were back into our books and loving our sports. Tia broke up with Willie's brother and we were all back hanging tight.

That didn't last long. When no one had boyfriends, we were bored with doing nothing, and Abby and I started doing other things like drinking cheap wine and shoplifting. We didn't have to steal because both of our moms had nice salaries, but stealing was fun and easy, and we were getting away with it. We started with lifting cheap wines. Mad Dog 20/20 was the easiest one to grab. We would each grab a bottle and sip on it, and after two sips we would be drunk. We started taking bottles with us to the volleyball games and sharing with our teammates or anyone else who wanted a drink.

We graduated from stealing cheap wine and took our shoplifting to the next level. We moved on to malls and small stores. We would hit the grocery stores for T-bone steaks and whatever we wanted to eat that day. I cooked, Abby and Charlie liked my cooking. Abby was always eager for my cooking. She said that it was to die for. Abby's mom didn't do a lot of cooking. They ate a lot of macaroni and cheese, so when she came to our house we pigged out. I made dinner and baked cakes. We would finish our meals with Mad Dog 20/20. All in all, we were good kids, just doing what teenagers did.

We didn't like what other girls our age were into, like having sex. We just loved shoplifting. It had become an addiction and boys were out for me. I never wanted a boy around me again sexually. My passion was now for clothes. I had to have all the Izod clothes. It was the early eighties and it was hot. I even had their socks. I then realized how profound my love for clothes was. My mother never bought me cheap clothes. We rarely shopped at the local K-mart. One time she'd given me her credit card and told me that I could spend five hundred dollars on school clothes. I was fourteen years old. I took her credit card to the mall, everything that I liked was costly, especially for a teenager. I only found a few pieces that I wanted and could afford. I left the mall with two outfits, a jacket, and one pair of shoes. Moreover, I ended up losing my mother's card. When I got home, momma tore me up for losing the card and for only having those two outfits. She made me take the clothes back, and with the money I spent, she found several outfits for me. She taught me how to look on the sales rack; I discovered they had some nice pieces at discount prices.

I always wanted the latest fashions, new arrivals. My shoplifting helped feed my expensive taste for fashion. I had all the hottest Lacoste and Izod clothes on top of what my mother was also buying me. I always wanted more, and I got just that.

My older cousins were also fly, and I loved to be around them. The oldest of the three girls was always my favorite. Her name was Tabby. The middle sister was named Gail and the youngest was Vickie. They also had four brothers. My sister Charlie and I always stayed at their house. They lived on 40th Ave. We called it "the block," and it was going down on the other side of the street all the time. Those cats had all the weed that you wanted to smoke and liquor. My cousin Vickie smoked weed and was the wildest out of the three girls. Gail and Tabby didn't smoke. All the dudes around town liked them. They were fly girls but they couldn't wear pants because my aunt was very religious. Vickie, as I stated being the wild one, would change into jeans at school. Tabby looked like Diana Ross with her long, lovely feathered hair. All the older men liked her; I would sit back and absorb the game that she had.

Vickie would be the one to turn me on to smoking weed and drinking Hennessy. I would get high and drunk with her all the time. Gail, the middle sister, was a good girl and never got into trouble or did no wrong. She would always tell Vickie that I was too young to be out smoking and drinking, but Vickie would still let me do it. Tabby was super fly. She had her booster, and would always buy me things. Sergio Valente, Jordache, and Levi jeans were the bomb in those days for the teens whose parents could afford it. I started partying with my older cousins with my new gear on. Now and then my brother Greg would catch me out at some of those parties and lose his mind. I thought I was grown, so I was going to do what grown people do.

My mother would send me to the parties to watch my sister Charlie, I didn't care what she was doing, I danced alone watching what the older teens did, so I could learn to do it better.

Chapter 3
Lost & Turned Out

A couple of years later, my life took a U-turn. My family moved to Kansas City, Missouri, which is when the shit hit the fan. My mother stayed in Omaha for a little longer to wait on transfer papers from her job at the Hospital. I lived with my aunt until momma came down. The guys in my new neighborhood liked Charlie and me. I never dated, but I thought I was mature and ready to explore. I was young, but I still wanted a man with a car. It was just so different in Kansas City than in Omaha and I liked it.

We would walk around the corner to the park and arcade. All the guys would ask my cousin Dede who we were. They would say that my sister and I were two chocolate, nice-looking sisters. My sister had a small waist and a big ass, and the men went crazy over it. I wasn't blessed like she was in that area, but I did have a pretty face, stomach, and breasts. Plus, I had the gift to gab like Charlie. We were the new chocolate drops in the city. We knew that we were about to run the town. That's just what we did. Queen and Charlie. Where she was, I was. We were the dynamic duo. That was us, ready for the world and everything in it. Only thing, I was dealing with bummy niggas before I ever got to the ballers, cats that never left the neighborhood but I thought had it going on. Guys that was way too old to be dealing with me, and other girls in the neighborhood, now I know that they were pedophiles, some even rapist.

When I started school, a lot of the girls would be jealous. They didn't too much care for the "new girl" in town. Plus, their men were all over me. I didn't have time to be tripping with those hood chicks who wanted beef with me. I was there to learn. The school was so different in K.C. because it was mostly black kids. There were a lot of black teachers as well. My old city Omaha had half black and half white students and all white teachers. K.C. was opposite.

I fit in well at school and in the neighborhood. My aunt lived in the "hood" 34th and Olive, where a lot took place. She gave me a little more freedom than momma did. I could come and go as I pleased, and because of this, I became fast as hell. I met a guy whose brother was the guy my cousin Dede was dating. We started messing around and eventually started having sex, plus I had started sleeping with a guy around the corner that took it, but I went back. I liked my cousins' boyfriend brother though, I liked him so much, he became my boyfriend, at least that's what I thought. He had other girls, but I thought I was in love, like any young girl that had someone digging her. By this time, my mom had moved to K.C., which stopped me from seeing him as much. I thought he was a good guy, but I started hearing stories about how he was out south where he was from. Doing raunchy shit like undercover robberies. We hung out for less than a year and parted ways. I didn't want a man that stole from people. My motto even when I was young, "get your own shit and make your own money."

Years later, he was murdered. I don't know why, but if he was robbing people, karma was bound to catch up with him. I moved in with my mother and transferred to Lincoln Preparatory Academy School. This transition helped me start getting back on track. Before my mom moved to K.C., I was having a ball hanging out with Charlie and Deedee and doing whatever the hell I wanted to do.

Lincoln High School is where I met my son's father. He was a nerd. He was obsessed with Run DMC, he stayed Adidas down, and what drew me to him was the fact that he starred on the basketball team. He was six-foot-four with nice hair. I liked him because he was very kind, cute, and a senior, I was a sophomore, and I always wanted older guys. We started dating and shortly after that I ended up pregnant. I was so young and not ready. I didn't tell my mom until I was six months pregnant and it was too late to do anything about it. I ended up moving in with him and his parents. After the baby arrived I stayed close to home for a while but I was itching to get back out in those streets with Charlie.

I started staying away from my boyfriend, and I eventually moved in with my sister. I went back to my old ways of kicking it: stealing, smoking, and drinking. By this time, it was going down. I had left Lincoln High School and started going to school at the teenage pregnancy center. There, I met Jamie, Kelli, and Marsha, who would become some of my lifelong friends. We were from the south side and thought we knew everything. We were young, pregnant, and fly, kind of like a lifetime movie. The chicks from the north side envied us, but we were also tough, and they knew not to fuck with our crew, pregnant or not.

My crew was hardcore and battle-tested bitches. We had our baby's months apart. Little B was born, and one of the best babies that I ever saw, with a young mom that didn't know how to really care or love him the way he was supposed to be loved. I didn't even know how to love myself. He was with me while I got back into the streets, and I left him home with my sister if he wasn't with his father.

When Little B turned two, he got sick with pneumonia. After he got out of the hospital, his dad wanted him to move in with him. He said that I wasn't doing right by him and that he would be a much better parent. I was young and trying to run the streets rather than being a mother, so I let Little B's father take him. I was still in school but didn't go as much. I met a guy that would change my life. My sister lived in a building on Thirtieth and Campbell where everyone smoked crack, and the guys sold drugs and made a lot of cash. I decided that I wanted cash like that, fast money. My homeboy Reggie had a drug connect out of California and he was doing his thing. I told him about the building and asked him if he could supply me with drugs. He was right on it and brought me a sandwich bag full of rocks, bagged up.

They were grams and eight balls; He told me what was what. After he schooled me, I caught on quick. I started slangin' twenties, fifties, and eight balls. I learned to listen to all of the cats hustling. They all told me something different to do. I took something out of what they all said and did things my way, and mastered the game. I started dealing hard, re-upping and saving my small drug dealing money. The first day of serving the dope fiends the crack, I made six-hundred dollars. I thought, "Wow, this is a lot of money, that quick in one day." It had only taken five hours to make it. By the time the sun went down, I was up eighteen-hundred dollars, but I still had to give my plug, one thousand dollars, of what I made. It was cool, though, because I had never made eight-hundred dollars of my own in one day. I was only sixteen.

I was doing my thing. I thought by the next week I would be doing well. I had good dope, and crack heads were everywhere. With all the crack heads running around like zombies, it reminded me of "The Walking Dead." During the day, they would sleep and eat up everything, but at night it was literally night of the living dead.

Charlie and I were doing our thing. If I was eating, then she was too. It was the same for her because she always looked out and took care of me as a big sister does. She was with her second son's daddy at this point. He was cool as hell but had started smoking the crack that we were selling. Charlie was in love with him but would soon have to cut him loose because he was stealing our weed, rocks, and money.

One time I smoked a primo with him. To be honest, I smoked primo several times and didn't realize that even though it was mixed with weed, I was still smoking crack cocaine, and that was a no-no! Once I even tried a joint of sherm stick, also called PCP or angel dust. PCP is associated with compulsive abuse. It's a recreational drug and can be ingested orally, smoked, or insufflated injected, but I couldn't handle any of that, I thank God that I stuck to smoking weed and getting my hustle on. We named the building on Thirtieth and Campbell the "Wild

Wild West." We had it on lock: rolling rocks, eight balls, and sixteenth. I thought crack heads were so stupid the way they would keep coming to get rocks instead of buying the whole eight ball. I didn't tell them, though, because I wanted all their money and this way I doubled up.

Chapter 4
Good Girl Gone Bad

The product was so good I was up about a thousand dollars of my own money! I would spend three hundred dollars on tennis shoes. I always kept on a fresh pair of kicks. Nike, Fila, Reebok, British Knights, Lottos, or whatever brand was hot. I didn't have to buy clothes because we were still boosting and we were fly all the time. By this time, I met a guy at school named Hassan that everyone was digging, and somehow, I snatched him up! I had it like that; young and bossy, and I demanded attention, even at a young age. He became my man. We thought we were in love. In those days, I thought that in a relationship, I had to be in love, but we weren't. His baby momma also went to the school. We never had a beef, but I knew she didn't like the fact that I was with her baby daddy and that I was younger. He was from my neighborhood, but I never saw him around. We would hang out and kick it in our hood. We would also go layup at my sister's house, chill, drink, smoke, and most times have sex. His sex game was proper; plus, it was better than any of the others I'd been with. He talked to me while he was up in it, telling me everything that a young girl like me wanted to hear. After he broke me off, I would tell myself that he was going to be my husband. He kept me coming for more. We kicked it for a year or so. Hassan was a tough guy that would knock anyone out that got in his way or talked shit to him. He was small, but he was a hard hitter. Niggas knew to get out of his way, and that attracted me even more.

Hassan started coming over with his boys. He and I were becoming distant because he had way too many chicks. I heard so much about what he had going on. Some of the females were only telling me because they were jealous and wanted him for themselves. Hassan had chicks all over, from out south to down north, and I wasn't competing with any broads. With all he had going on, I was spring, so I stayed down and was faithful to him. We were a cute couple, but we weren't meant for each other. For one, all the girls in the school liked him, and for two, he was a bad boy.

I wanted to find a working guy at this point and not a thug, even though I was a little hood. A regular man would balance me out and get me back on track. When Hassan graduated, we were still together, but he got crazier, fighting and having shoot-outs. We were smoking primos together, getting drunk, and doing everything that a dysfunctional couple could do. The more he fought, the more girls he got; Girls in my city loved gangsters. A gangster had a better chance at women than a working man, at least in the circle of chicks that I hung around. I started trying to see other cats and focus on my money-making. I was finally on track with my cash again. I let him do what he was doing with all the girls and finally gave up the relationship. It's like when you get a man; no one likes him until he has a chick. He always had a lot of chicks, but it got worse.

One day he was hanging out, and he got shot. He got messed up pretty bad, and that's when we grew apart. One of the guys that would come by with Hassan, Jon-Jon, was still coming through even when Hassan and I stopped kicking it. We started hanging out. First, we just drank together, and then we started messing around. Hassan said I did him wrong by kicking it with his boy, and maybe I did, but in my eyes, they became good friends after he was shot. Another truth: He shot himself messing around carelessly with his own gun. I had never seen Jon-Jon with him before the month he got shot. It was a done deal, and Jon-Jon and I were dating. Hassan started dating my friend. Fuck it; we swapped it out. Jon-Jon was feeling me but had a lot of cons. He had a lot of women and a girlfriend that would pop up tripping on a regular. I was tripping too. I felt if he was hers, how the hell was he at my house screwing me every day? Well, that's what some men do and he was one of them. The chick and I were lightweight beefing, but she didn't want any of this, so she ran her mouth from the street sending subliminal messages through people and never ran up on me. I told her to check her man. It wasn't looking good for her.

I was still on my mission and doing it big. After a year of dating, Jon-Jon and I were always fighting. He was messing around, so I started doing the same thing. As they say, just the way you get him, someone else will take him. Jon-Jon would follow me and do all types of dumb shit. He was a crazy ass alcoholic, but since I was in love with him, I overlooked his flaws. After all, I wasn't perfect. Jon-Jon's hustle was stealing cars and selling drugs. The year before I met him, he was somewhere in college in St. Joseph, Missouri. I would have settled for the old Jon-Jon. He was a good guy gone bad. Jon-Jon and Hassan were terrorizing the streets, shooting at people and getting shot at. Jon-Jon was shot about seven times while we were together.

God was always with him. He had a colostomy bag that he had to wear for a while. Some guys ran up on him one day on 35th and Prospect, shooting up the block and shooting him up bad. There were always shoot-outs in our hood. It was a mess, like living in Iraq, and they were the Taliban. It was so bad that one day one of the little homies Goofy was murdered at the gas station. Some older cats were looking for Shon. Goofy would always jump in the car with me or any of the older chicks and cats that hustled. He was a little hustler and stayed hanging with the older crowd. This day was a bad day. He was sitting in the car while Shon went and paid for gas. The shooters pulled up busting several rounds off into the car and at the gas station. They were trying to hit Shon but hit Goofy instead. It was so sad because he was a like a nephew to me and he was only fourteen. I was cool with his family. His cousin J.C. was my best friend, and I called him my brother. I felt their pain. Jon-Jon lived across the street from them and was very close to the whole family. They were just like his family so after that, Jon-Jon was on a mission, ready to take the life of the man that robbed Goofy of his life.

I was head over heels for Jon-Jon, so I was down for anything he did, wrong or right. I was his ride or die chick. I was seventeen and felt like I finally found true love. We were in shoot-outs so bad that the car would be wrangled with bullets. By the graces of God, no one was hurt or hit. There was a lot going on in my life. I got a call from my cousin, Vickie, back in Omaha, and she told me that she had just seen my father on the news. She was hysterical. I told Vickie to calm down and start over. While she was telling me, what happened, I fired up my blunt and listened to what she had to say. She told me that my father was on the news and that he had murdered his girlfriend. I put the blunt out asking, "What? Are you sure that it's my daddy?" Vickie replied, "Yes, it's your dad." She told me that he had on a pair of Levi jeans and an Oakland A's ball cap.

She said that the news reported that he had a gun in his hand while arguing with his girlfriend. He shot the gun at the ground, and the bullet ricocheted and hit her in the chest. The news also reported that he stayed by her side and tried to resuscitate her while he called the police. He never left her side. The paramedics pronounced her dead. I couldn't believe what I was hearing. I wanted to cry, for her and daddy. It appeared to be an accident, but she was someone's mother, and I know how I would have felt if something like that ever happened to my mother.

Charlie and I headed to Omaha to see what was going on and if there was something we could do. I felt so bad for her children because they were a little younger than me and I knew they were hurting. When we arrived in the city, my dad was being released. We met up with him and gave him a big hug. We told him that we loved him and that everything would be okay. Daddy didn't talk about it, and we didn't ask questions.

Before heading back to K.C., we stopped by my cousin Vickie's house and talked to her. We smoked blunts and sipped on Remy Martin. I needed to smoke to clear my mind. There was just a lot going on, and

God knows I didn't need any more news. My phone rang, and for some reason, I didn't want to answer. I knew that I had to, so I answered, and J.C. said that Jon-Jon had just been shot and that I needed to get to the hospital because it wasn't looking good for him.

I told him that I was out of town checking on my dad and that I would get on the road right away. I immediately started crying and praying. I loved Jon-Jon, and I didn't want him to die. Despite all the arguments and cheating, I knew that he was my soul mate and he had to live. I left Omaha and sped all the way back to K.C. Charlie kept telling me to slow down before we crashed and died. I hoped my man wouldn't die. I drove straight to the hospital to be by his side. It was after hours and the nurse told me that I would have to come back in the morning. I explained to her that I was his fiancé and that I had just gotten into town. Fiancé got me in. She felt sorry and let me go in to see him. Charlie stayed in the waiting room because she didn't want to see him like that. He had just gotten out of surgery and was just waking up. I walked into the room and immediately broke down on my knees and started praying. My man looked so vulnerable lying there with all those tubes attached. Out of all the times, he had been shot, none compared to this.

He looked at me, weak, with a tear in his eye, shaking his head. He was unable to speak, but he could comprehend and was aware of what was happening. I had never seen Jon-Jon cry, but he was in pain and bad shape! He was shot three times in his upper body. It would take him months to recover. He had all kind of flowers being delivered, and chicks were coming up to the hospital to see him. I didn't have time to trip with him about that. I was just happy that he didn't die. I didn't have time to babysit him or worry about his groupies. I had to get back to my grind.

By this time, I was up to nine ounces of my own. In my eyes, I was the shit! I and my sister were the "it" girls, and we were in high demand. My sister had a guy she needed to shake. The building we lived in turned him out, into an addict. The crack had gotten to him. He hit that pipe and couldn't put it down. It was sad because before that he was cool, but no one wanted a crack head around. We had to break away from that scene, and Charlie had to shake her man. We moved away from the building, and I got my weight up. For a young girl in the late eighties, everyone knew I was the up and coming, Queen of the city.

Dudes got at me and had work, and they told me they would hook me up for a good price. Then another one would come lower. It was like Wal-Mart comparing prices. I would give the highest price and get the one with the best deal. That way, I could make a thousand dollars or more.

One day we were on the West side making deals, and this nigga that liked my sister took some money from me and tried to talk slick because I was young. He bullied everyone around, and even though he was a grown man, I knew that I couldn't fight him. I called my OG homeboys that looked out for me, and everyone in the town respected them and let them know what this nigga had done to me. It didn't take them long to pull up and ask Stan what kind of punk shit he was on. Just because I was young and a woman didn't mean he should disrespect the game! Stan jumped fly and left them no choice but to pistol whip him. His head cracked open, and there was blood everywhere. They told Stan not to ever fuck with me again, or his family would find him somewhere stinking. He knew they meant business. After that, he didn't even want to deal with Charlie. He said I was too much and fast for my age, and that he had to stay away from us. Charlie didn't trip because I was her little sister, and she knew that nigga was dead wrong. I knew that I was a boss chick and if people fucked with me, I had folks to set them straight. After the dudes whipped his ass, Stan did a bitch move. He went and told my mom that I was suspended from school for selling weed and that I was a drug dealer. My mom started asking me questions about where I was getting money. I told her I got it from men, which was the truth, just not the whole truth. Then I met some chicks that I thought were as bossy as Charlie and me, a nice little crew. Between me, Charlie, and their crew, we were hot and couldn't be stopped. We were balling like a gang in the city, and every cat in the city wanted a piece of one of us. It was on. We were going to the skating rinks, clubs, hell anywhere it was popping. I turned eighteen, but I was the shit. People thought I was older because my sister and cousins were. I had a grown woman's mind.

In 1987-88, I was rolling, but everything came to a screeching halt when I got pregnant. At four months, my unborn child's father, Jon-Jon, got caught up in Los Angeles, California trying to bring back two kilos of cocaine. Everyone was bringing drugs back on the plane. I guess he had done it before, so he was trying his luck again. He got caught and was arrested. Then I found out that one of my best friends, Shara, had been sleeping with him all along. Shara claimed she was a virgin, but she screwed my child's father. Out of all the men that wanted her, she wanted mine, and his scandalous ass bit the bait. My friend, Dana was tough and a red bone. She didn't take any mess. Dana always said that she knew Shara wasn't right, but I didn't want to believe her. She didn't say anything because she didn't want me talking smack saying she was jealous because I was hanging out with a new crew.

It was true that Shara and Jon-Jon were sleeping together behind my back. I was cooler with Shara than I was with all the other broads in her crew, so she was the last one I thought would stab me in my back. But a bitch will be a bitch, and when chicks saw how good Jon-Jon took care of me, I guess they wanted to walk in my shoes. After that, I went cold turkey on all of them. Where I was trying to go didn't match with what they had going on. I broke apart from them and went my own way. It was back to loyalty, my ride or dies. Trecie was down from day one. She was Charlie's son's father's sister and people thought she was our blood sister. She was down with Charlie and me and had our backs. I also had my friend Dana. Dana and I met through Jon-Jon years back and clicked. He was her man but I was her homegirl, and we were loyal to each other.

Dana also had a crew of her own. They were east side chicks but would get it in if they had to. I liked her crew; we never had issues. Jon-Jon ended up going to prison in California. Although I was pregnant with his baby, I didn't care. He betrayed me by sleeping with Shara. He wouldn't get one piece of mail from me. I hated him, and I was going to get the last laugh on both of those snakes! At this point, my friends Dana and Donna started dating Hassan. Dana and Donna didn't hang and really didn't know each other. It was a crazy coincidence that I loved them both, and they both felt the same about me. They were both infatuated with Hassan's no-good ass, but his sex was on point. After all, he was mine years before.

We never discussed what went on between Hassan and me. I was screwing his friend, so I guess that made us even.

Hassan was Dana's man, and Donna knew that he was feeling Dana, even though he messed around. Other chicks catered to him and bought him shit, but Dana didn't! He was a gigolo. I became very good friends with Donna through Shara's crew. She was loyal, unlike the rest of them. They were all cousins and slept with the same guys. It's bad enough to mess with a friend's man, but sleeping behind your family, DAMN.

Donna hung with them, and we became very good friends. I would stay at her house, and she would stay at mine. She had a great family. Her brother had just been murdered, so I was helping her get through the tragic ordeal, her little sisters loved me, and I loved them. I would tell Donna that her youngest sister was going to be a G like her and the other one would probably be married somewhere, and we would laugh. She was loyal, and a true gangster and could boost her ass off. That was right up my alley. Hassan wasn't an issue because I was young when I was with him, and he was a player. Hassan and my baby daddy were best friends, so that chapter in my book was closed. Hassan always said that when he got shot, I left him, but the truth was that he was a whore and I couldn't take all the lying and cheating that he was doing. I was tired of being stepped on, even though Jon-Jon was no different, maybe even worse.

I met a heavy hitter soon after. He was heavy as well. I liked me a fat boy and still do. His name was Lucky, and he started coming around. We would sit in the car and talk for hours. I met Lucky when I was out one night with Trecie, Charlie, and J.C. at a rinky-dink club off 39th and Prospect. A guy came over to me and that the guy across the room wanted to know what I was drinking. He had to know I was pregnant because I was nice and plump. Charlie was also pregnant with her third child. Our kids would only be months apart. She was working on three, and I was about to have two. I told him to send the waitress over and that we would order what we wanted to drink. Trecie and J.C. ordered a Tom Collins and Charlie, and I had mixed fruit juice. After Lucky sent us a few rounds, he came over to the table and talked to me. He introduced himself and let me know that he already knew who I was. He had a cool, slick voice with a slick laugh.

He told me that he had been checking me out for a year or so and that he knew I had a man, a crazy ass man at that. He said that he didn't believe in stepping on anybody's toes, but he wanted to see what was up with me. Lucky asked me if I was still with Jon-Jon. I told him no, but that I was expecting his child soon. I also told him how Jon and Shara were sleeping together behind my back and that Jon-Jon could go to hell! It felt good to talk to him and get that off my chest. I was still angry about the situation. We talked for a while and exchanged numbers. Lucky and I talked all the time and started dating.

We didn't have sex because I was about to drop my second child. He never even tried to touch me until after I delivered. He helped me out a lot. I liked him, and he gave me whatever I asked for, which wasn't much because I was still doing my thing. He was a blessing to me and my soon to be born child. I couldn't wait to have my baby, so I could get back to hustling.

I finally delivered my beautiful daughter the day after my birthday, June 9, 1988. She was gorgeous and healthy. I thought about Jon-Jon and wished that he was around to see her be born. Even though I was mad at him, I knew that he would have been a good father and he deserved to see this great gift of joy that God had given us. It was on with Lucky and me after Angel was born.

He would come through, and we would chill for hours. We would lay around and cuddle. I still couldn't have sex for six weeks, but I was for sure ready, and I was going to break Lucky off when it was time. He had already waited for half of my pregnancy, which meant he had to care about me, and I cared for him. Lucky would always leave to meet with people. He was a go-getter who was moving kilos of cocaine like it wasn't a thing.

One day, I was changing Lucky's tape player in the trunk of his Cadillac. It was crazy how we had to go to the trunk to change the music back then, but that was only if you were a boss with the player in the back! Thank God for modern day technology. Lucky had so much money; I couldn't believe my eyes. There were trash bags full of it. I was young and had never seen that much money in my life, at least not in person. It was amazing. I was getting money, but he had trash bags full of cash! I only had a couple of Crown Royal bags. I asked him how I could be down. He told me that I wasn't ready and to stay in the minor leagues because he was most definitely in the major league. We had a very long homie, lover, friend relationship. While we were kicking it, through it all, he still had a lot of other chicks and several baby mommas. One of his baby mommas didn't like me, but who cared? She wasn't my friend, but I was checking for her man. I kicked it with a few men, but not all of them received sex from me, just a whole lot of game.

When you have a mouth piece like I did, you could get anything out of a man with absolutely nothing in return, and yes, I had the gift to gab, and I used it to my advantage. Now, I knew that I was a master manipulator. All the cats with money knew that I was getting money too, and they liked a woman that could hustle. I was the lady hustler of the year, the "Queen B." I was in high demand and could pull any man I wanted.

I'd always lived with my sister, so I finally got my own spot. Lucky helped me get an apartment on the north side, where I lived with my daughter. It was a nice, one-bedroom apartment and I had it looking nice. Even though Angel's dad was gone, he had boys that helped me furnish my apartment. It was nothing expensive, but always clean and, cozy. We were good. The apartment where I lived was a blood neighborhood, and that's what I was down with. I was claiming Blood. I fit right in, and everything I wanted and needed was close by.

I started selling cocaine and weed again but not at my apartment because Lucky would be tripping about that. He was in the game way longer than I was, and he was way smarter. He, told me never do business where you lay your head, especially when children were involved. I always listened because he kept it real all the time. I would go to a part of the apartment complex called the crack and make at least a thousand dollars a day or better, and I had Lucky to help me. He bought me clothes, shoes, groceries, and wined and dined me all the time. He was my big teddy bear and had I known what I know now; I would have been saving for a rainy day.

Luck's sex was magnificent. For a big guy, he knew how to get me wet and make me come. He was the first person to ever eat my pussy. Back in the late 80s and early 90s, sucking dick and eating pussy was not the thing to do, and when a woman was accused of sucking dick, everyone talked bad about her, and she was a nasty hoe. I remember the night Lucky and I got drunk at the Jones' place. We drank Tom Collins all night. I was smoking joints. We barely made it home, but once we got to my apartment, we went at it. We never made it to the bedroom. We undressed, kissed, and got freaky. He was sticking his fingers in and out of my pussy. I was wet as hell, and then he did something that I wasn't ready for but went along with. He took his two wet fingers out of me, put them in my mouth, and told me to taste it. I'd never tasted myself. As not to disturb the mood, I did as I was told. It turned him on to see how wet he made me, so he stuck his fingers back inside of me, sucked on them, and said, "Damn baby, that pussy is super wet, and you taste good as fuck!" He threw my legs up and started kissing on my titties. He kissed along my body, inching closer to my pussy. He started sucking on it. I felt like I was in heaven. He fucked me with is tongue, and I fucked his tongue just like I was fucking a dick. I had never felt so liberated. It felt so damn good that I saw stars. I squirted, damn near knocking him backward. I was embarrassed because my pussy had never done what he made it do, but he slurped it all up. I think it made him like me more. After he made me come multiple times, I made him come. He fucked me so good from the front that I didn't trip off him putting his tongue in my mouth with all my juices over his mouth and his face. We went at it for a full hour and fell asleep without bothering to wash off. Every time we had sex, I must say, it was explosive. When I say he earned his name, that's what I mean. Mr. Hall of Fame.

Regardless of how good the sex was, the relationship was just a friendship thing. He didn't claim me, and I didn't claim him. He did his thing, and I did mine. I didn't care about his other chicks as long as he treated me right. I was a player just like him. After Jon-Jon messed with my friend, my heart was cold, and I turned into a beast. I felt like I couldn't love another man like that again and they all had to bow down to me. It was my way or the highway. I treated niggas like they treated chicks: bad, and they liked it. I was acting just like the niggas, heartless with no conscience. I had to do me, and that's exactly what I did.

I started chilling with other cats, but they couldn't handle me, and my mouth was too slick for them. Cats didn't know how to step to me, but they still tried. I was a boss lady, and they weren't ready for me. No man wants to see a woman do better than them, but that was me, not your ordinary chick. I was a rare breed. Most men were intimidated by me. They knew if they didn't have the cash to not even look my way. I'm not saying I was a gold digger, but I wasn't fucking with any broke niggas. If a cat was broke, didn't have a car, or lived at home with his momma, we didn't have the same goals. I had my own money, so that's how it was, either you were with me, above me, or against me.

While I was playing and doing my thing, my best friend Donna was out doing some illegal activities to get her boo Hassan out of jail. She fell hard for him and would do anything for his no-good ass, including taking penitentiary chances. She had Hassan all the latest Adidas gear that came out. Whatever he wanted he got if she could get her hands on it. I never liked giving my money to men, and I thank God that I didn't get the tricking off on men syndrome because I watched chicks give men their cash all the time. Shit, I was looking for help. Don't get me wrong, if a man helped me, I would for sure return the favor, just not by giving up my money.

Donna was still hustling and got caught up with some credit card and check fraud scam at work. A warrant was issued for her arrest. Donna said that she wasn't going to jail and her damn sure wasn't going to turn herself in. She said that if they wanted her that they would just have to find her. She went on the run instead of turning herself in. After Donna left, I started hanging back out, going to the clubs, and going to the skating rink. The rink was in North Kansas City. Everybody got fly and could choose up, or get chosen at the rink. My homegirls and I would go every Sunday. Mika and Ree were a little younger than I was but they were my down homegirls. Trecie was always with me when we went skating. We never skated, we stood around, looking fly, while all the ballers tried to holla at us. If there was one we liked, he might get lucky enough to take us out or get us to stop by the house and let me, Trecie, and Tabby smoke up his weed, and it had better be that chronic. If they didn't have that good Cali bud, we called them lames. I and my crew stopped smoking regular weed in 1992. All the Cali boys were bringing that chronic in town, spoiling us with the exotic taste, and after I tasted that fresh pine, I didn't want any more Bobby Brown, as we called it, or seeds to pop on my new fresh gear.

Donna would call every now and then to let me know that she was okay and as soon as she had enough money to pay a lawyer that she would turn herself in and that everything would be back right. I told her that with the money we had, we could pay down on a lawyer and that she should come home and just get it over with. It couldn't have been that serious. While Donna was on the run, she met a guy and started falling for him. She hadn't told him that she was on the run yet because she didn't want to mess her good thing up. I understood and told her to be careful, and that I loved her and was praying for her. I missed Donna. She would go into Dillard's when she was around and get us bags of the most fly clothes. Donna could dress her ass off. She also was a fighter. I remember one day when we were at Swope Park, and some chicks who didn't like us because their men were checking for us started tripping and making a scene. They thought that because they were the main chicks that they could get something off. We didn't have anything serious going on with any of the cats; no one was even sleeping with them. They were ballers doing big numbers. We would just go hang out with them, smoke, and chill. Their chicks knew that we were hot girls and they weren't feeling us hanging out with their men. Plus, they were certified, country Kansas City chicks, and if I hadn't known that they were from Missouri, I would have thought that their country asses were from Kansas. With the ugly ass clothes and fucked up hairdos, they sure knew how to pick them, but when I look back they were country as hell too, they just had money. We got to the park, and they tried to front on us. Donna always carried a shotgun in her car and would use it if she had to. There were about five chicks and three of us. We started fighting and ended up whipping their asses without even a scratch. Donna pulled out that shotgun and beat one of the chicks all upside her head with it. After the fight was over, we laughed and gave Donna the name "shotgun D." That was her new name, and she liked it.

Everyone knew not to step to us with any bullshit because we would fight and Donna would be ready to shoot that shotgun. On another note, the cats whose chicks we were fighting in the park that day ended up getting indicted on a conspiracy to distribute cocaine. That got them forty and sixty-five-year federal prison sentences. I always wondered how someone could get more time for selling dope then for murder. It was such a bad thing. The feds were taking the city down. President George W. Bush was not playing, and President Reagan had set in place a war on drugs and African Americans were getting slammed with football numbers. All the D-boys were getting caught up, and their girlfriends were getting locked up too. I knew that everybody was getting caught up and knew that it could happen to me, but I kept grinding and thought that I'd worry about it when the time came. I thought to myself that they were only getting caught because they were dealing with large quantities of drugs. I was on a lower scale. They had birds, and I just dealt in four and a half and nines breaking them down. Rock cocaine carried more time than powder, so that meant I would receive more time than the ones with the significant weight. I thought I might as well step my game up. I was doing my thing, playing with half of birds or less, but for a young chick, I was doing my thing, and it was getting better. I cooked up my own dope and everything. Reggie and Jon-Jon taught me how to cook up my own work, so I didn't have to pay someone to do it which meant more money for me to keep.

I prayed that I would never get caught or robbed all the time. The jackers were out and didn't give a damn who they robbed, shit; they stole from their own mommas.

It was time for the annual player's ball to roll around. We had one every year, and they would crown a new player who the city thought was balling the hardest. I started preparing myself for the festivities and thought about what I could wear. Trecie said that she would go to the mall and grab us a few outfits and we could pick out which ones we wanted to rock. Lucky was also shopping for something to wear. He was big, but that never stopped him from being fly wearing fly big boy shit. Lucky always smelled good. I loved me a big sexy man that smelled good!

The weekend didn't come fast enough. It was time for the players' ball. I wore a five-hundred-dollar Ellen Tracy blouse. We didn't care who the designer was; We went for the most expensive clothes in the stores. I didn't give a damn about who created them. The blouse was an eye-catcher. I had big boobs so I would have all my cleavage out tonight and would look as sexy as I could for Lucky and whoever else was watching.

Trecie got her and Charlie outfits from a store that we had in the mall called Gantos. They had some nice pieces in there, and nothing cost less than two hundred dollars. Trecie could boost, and she made sure that it was worth stealing. I bought myself a one-hundred-and-ninety-dollar pair of Via Spiga's. I was ready for whatever. We went to the beauty shop, got our hair done together by Russie, and headed home. When I got home, I laid back in the tub and smoked on a Philly blunt. I decided to call Lucky and see what he found to wear. I knew that tonight he would deliver a wonderful presentation with whatever he chose to wear. He answered the phone and told me that he was handling some things and would call me back because he needed to talk to me about something. We hung up. I shaved and laid back in the warm water. I was thinking about coming back to the house with

Lucky after the ball and him loving me down with his hall of fame head that made me moist. Lucky gave the best head that I had ever had. I had a couple of guys that went downtown, but Lucky was the bomb diggity. He was the truth, straight hall of fame at eating the cat! He would put his tongue so far up my pussy and swirl it around; he gave me no other choice but to squirt all my juices into his mouth! As big as he was, I must give it to him, his sex was on point. They say fat boys don't know how to please a woman, but my fat boy was laying that pipe down. His pack wasn't small either. He had that whip appeal and satisfied my sexual appetite every time we made love.

I started getting dressed, did my make up, and headed out to the ball. Almost everybody was clean, and we sat there cracking jokes about the ones who weren't. I hated the Harold Penner two-piece suits with a passion, and a few of the OG's and youngsters had on the same country suit or a different color. I knew I wouldn't have on anything like anyone else. There was a gang of female boosters in the city, but their style wasn't like ours. They stole regular, ordinary shit out of Dillard's. We went into the parts of the mall that they didn't think about going into. We were having a ball, chatting and drinking with everyone. It was a very nice turnout, and things were organized well. My girls and I were laughing. Trecie was saying that I should be the one getting the player of the year award. She said I went harder than a lot of these fake ballers and asked how they even got trophies. Tommy had been selling ounces for six years and couldn't even get his money up to buy a nine because he was trying to look fly. He was running for player of the year. With all those rings on every finger, I was wondering the same thing, but I was a chick and all the players that won awards were men. If there had been a category for both, I would have won for sure.

Lucky finally showed up and looked like a big bag of money. All I could do was smile. I told Charlie that I was leaving with Lucky. Charlie said they planned on going to the after-hours spot when they left the ball. The only thing I was thinking about doing after the ball was going back to my place with Lucky and banging it out in the bed. As quick as I started smiling, I started frowning. A chick came out of nowhere and stood by his side. It was his woman. I knew he had other chicks, and I didn't mind that, but this was the first time that I ever saw him with one. My feelings were hurt, but I kept my composure and kept doing what I was doing. I turned my swagger up to the next level. Lucky watched me all night, and I knew it so I talked to a few of the D-boys and acted like I was interested to make him as jealous as I could, but I wasn't interested at all. Trecie told me to leave Lucky alone because he was no good for me. I knew he was no good for me, but I was still dealing with him. If a guy liked me too much, I wouldn't mess with him. I only messed with cats that were a challenge for me. The dudes that liked me, I could run over, but the ones I liked gave me a real challenge, and I loved a rebellious man. I wasn't the only female that had this issue, but I was a straight drama queen. After a few drinks, I was ready to go home and chill. I was tired of watching Lucky flaunt around with his girl. It made me mad because she was a wet head who smoked sherm and crack. With all the money he had, he was here with a crack head. She was cute, but a fiend nonetheless.

After the king was crowned the player of the year, I was ready to get the hell out of that place. I needed to go and smoke some weed because I was pissed. I couldn't wait until we got home. I fired up right in the car. I thought about what happened and knew that one day it would come to this. I think Lucky was trying to tell me that he was coming with someone earlier when we spoke but he never called me back.

Later that evening I got a call from Lucky. I was pissed and didn't answer. I told Charlie and Trecie that Lucky could kiss my ass and go to hell. We laughed a little and smoked a little and went to bed. The next morning, I turned on the news. They were talking about a big drug bust that happened late the night before off Gregory and Prospect.

The news reported that there had been twelve men arrested on conspiracy charges. They kicked in all of their houses that morning and had been watching the men for more than a year. I was wondering who it could have been, knowing that I had to know them when the phone rang. J.C. was on the other end saying, "They got your boy Lucky late last night. The feds caught him with some bricks. He was meeting somebody and got hit. They said his ass is grass." I was crushed and scared because if they were watching him, they might have been watching me too! I jumped up and started gathering up the little drugs that I had around the house. I immediately took them to my cousin's house. It was a crazy day. I had just seen Lucky last night with another bitch and was pissed the hell off. Still, this wasn't the way I wanted to see him. As mad as I was, I didn't want anything like that to ever happen to him, or anyone else, but it did. The feds caught him, and they were surely going to make him pay. Man, I would miss him, and of course his dangerous tongue! After about a week, Lucky could get in touch with me. He told me to visit him at CCA in Leavenworth, Kansas because they wouldn't give him a bond. The feds labeled him a flight risk and kept him locked up. Lucky had a good run and now his operation was destroyed. He was sentenced to ten years and quickly shipped out of the city. That's the thing with the feds, they ship people out to the middle of nowhere and the sentence the hand down is usually very long. They take our black men, and women all around the world away from their families, separating us, only to become their slaves!

I was heartbroken. Lucky was my big teddy bear, and now he was gone on a conspiracy case, fighting for his life. I would have to settle for some Gerald Levert music and reminisce about the good times that we had. Everybody seemed like they were disappearing. Every time someone went to prison, another set of hustlers arrived. Just like revolving doors, they came in and went out. It seemed like everything was going wrong. Finally, we received good news. We got a call about our father. His murder case was thrown out. He was free and clear of the murder charges and never had to spend a day in jail. We were so relieved. He was a good man who made a mistake. We wrote the judge and told him how good of a father he was and that he didn't mean to kill his girlfriend. His girlfriend's kids also spoke to the judge and told him that they forgave my dad and that they knew it was an accident. I was glad, but if it had been my mom and a man killed her accidentally, I would have killed him accidentally.

Two months went by, and Donna started calling less and less. I felt for her and wanted her to come home. Donna was very attached to her family, and I knew she missed them, and they missed her. I knew that she also missed her girls. We played hard, and I wanted to have one of those play days with my girl. I missed her so much and just needed to speak with her about everything that was going on in my life. She always gave me good advice. We talked about everything, and now she wasn't calling. I started focusing on Angel and going to see Lil' B when his dad let me. The kids and I had fun together, and I bought them whatever they wanted. I was having some pretty good days with the kids, and it felt good to focus on them. They had all my attention, the way it always should have been.

After Lucky left, I chilled. I didn't really hang out with anyone. I wrote him a lot and wasn't interested in being bothered by the cats in the town. I was good. I hung around the house a lot and started reading books. Reading had become my hobby. It took my mind off everything. It relaxed me. One evening I was sitting around reading Sister Soldier's book, "*The Coldest Winter Ever*." I had Luther Vandross playing, "If This World Were Mine" in my own world. I was puffing on swisher sweet, drinking a wine cooler, when I received a call that I wish I would never have answered. There was a feeling in my gut that I only got when something was wrong. Donna's little sister was on the phone, and she was crying hysterically. I asked her if the police caught Donna and she screamed. I started crying too because I knew it was bad and I was a cry baby. She couldn't get out what she wanted to tell me. I cried with her because I felt her pain. I told her that if they caught Donna that it would be okay, at least she could get it over with and come home once she paid for what she did. She cried harder, and all I could do was pray. Momma always said that when the going gets rough, fall on your knees and pray. I didn't know what Donna's sister was going to say, but I prayed to prepare myself for whatever it was that I was about to hear. She finally screamed out, "He killed my sister!" I was puzzled for a moment. I dropped the phone, laid my head down and cried my eyes out. I couldn't believe that Donna was gone. She was a good girl, and I didn't understand why someone would want to hurt her. We later found out that the guy she was dating was on the run for murder. Donna was dating him without knowing he was wanted in Chicago. Come to find out, he brutally beat her to death with brass knuckles, rolled her up, and put her body in an abandoned building where it decomposed. I was sick to my stomach and so agonized about it. I thought about the last time I had seen my friend. She was walking out my door telling me that she had to go. She was dressed fly as usual with her banging short haircut, smiling like nothing was wrong, and everything would be alright. But it wasn't. She was going on the run. I never got to see her face again. I've never wished death on anyone, but when they told me that he had killed himself as well, I was relieved. He was a coward who took away an angel. I missed her dearly and I cried for weeks, wondering why so much in my life was going so wrong. I was sorrowful for her family. I talked to my mom about all the chaos that was going on in my life. I never told her about selling drugs, but deep down she knew. It never once changed the way she felt about me. She always told me to do the right thing and get a job. Momma hugged me and quoted a scripture: "Weeping may endure for a night, but joy comes in the morning" (Psalms 30:5). I was going to miss my girl. She was a true friend. Rest in Heaven, Donna.

After Donna passed away, I said that I was going to change and stop selling drugs, but I didn't. It got worse. Every man that wanted to claim me as their girl would have to give me whatever I asked for. I wanted it all, my money and theirs. I was on a money mission; all the play dating had stopped.

I wasn't in a serious relationship, so when Jon-Jon got out of jail, we got back together again. This time he proposed and said he'd be a better man. He was a wonderful father, and the thought of him being a better man was amazing. I was overjoyed; I was getting married! I was ready to settle down and be his wife. Charlie was about to marry her last child's father, and we were going to have a double wedding. I was excited. It was all a dream that became a nightmare. We called the wedding off because Jon-Jon was up to the same old bullshit. Shara started hating because he didn't want her shermed out smoking ass. We had bad fights. One night, my girls and I were at the club and ended up fighting Shara and her cousins. Shara stabbed Trecie pretty bad in her arm. We had to rush Trecie to Research hospital from the Jones' place. She was bleeding and losing lots of blood. I was driving as fast as I could to get to the hospital. There was blood dripping all over the car. Trecie was telling Charlie that she was gon' get that bitch, Shara. Thank God Trecie was okay. She had to get ten stitches in her arm. She was crunk and wanted to find Shara. We smoked a couple of blunts and drank a fifth of Remy Martin to calm Trecie down. We were most definitely going to get revenge on that bitch. She was out of line about a man that didn't want her. She wasn't anything more than a sex toy. Jon-Jon liked sex and was trying to screw whoever he could. He was fucking dang near everyone in their click. We were still together, holding on to hope, prayer, and a dream. I told Charlie if it didn't work with Jon-Jon this time that it would be the last. I was tired of going back to him knowing that he was never going to change. Charlie didn't believe me when I said I was going to leave him alone.

Every time Trecie saw Shara after the stabbing, she would beat her down. I was never with Trecie when she saw Shara because I still wanted to slap her for screwing my man. Jon-Jon and Shara were both sloppy, and I blamed him, as well.

After a year of holding on to an illusion, I gave up and got a new boyfriend. He was a young hot item. I was feeling him. His name was Shon. I had known Shon for a while back in the day when Goofy got murdered at the gas station on 35th and Prospect (the guy they were trying to hit was Shon). Shon took my mind away from the guys I'd dated or tried to date. We had explosive sex. Shon had what every woman wanted between her legs and knew how to work it. He made me feel energized and alive! We were into each other and Jon-Jon couldn't take it.

The crazy part was that the day I was supposed to be walking down the aisle was the very first time Shon and I slept together. Jon-Jon was trying to fight my new man and me. He hated Shon with a passion. You know what they say, "You never miss a good thing until it's gone," and that's what it was. I was gone and never turning back. Shon and I were together all the time. We never used condoms, so I got pregnant a few times and got abortions because I didn't want another child. I had two children already and was okay with the two I had. Shon wanted me to be his baby momma. He already had four or five kids and was still on a role. I didn't have any kids by his fertile ass. I told him that he needed a vasectomy, raw dogging shooting out babies. I needed the pill or I needed to make him strap up. I was just as much at fault, praying that he wouldn't give me a disease. The power of the D.

Shon's dad was a pimp, and he tried to be one too. It seemed like when I started messing with him, his stakes increased. Everyone wanted him. He was out there bad. He had a lot of chicks, but he gave me respect. In small cities like Kansas City, Missouri, you ended up sharing men because there were only a selective few that everyone wanted. In this town, it was five women to a man. I didn't want to share, but I had that don't give a fuck attitude, and I was used to men like him. All I could say was that I needed to choose my men wiser.

I wasn't tripping because I was doing me and I was making my money. I helped him out once or twice to come up with some cash, and he did. He became one of the bossiest cats in the city. He won the player of the year the next year. Once he hooked up with the Mexican that he told me about, she set him straight.

When Shon started making big money, his head got big. He was already cocky when he didn't have anything, but now his head was in the clouds. I was ready to break away. I hated to see someone go from nothing to something and forget how they got there, and who helped them get there. I was getting my money, but my attitude remained the same, always. I was true to the game. I treated everyone the same whether I had the money or not.

The months were going by fast and Shon, and I was doing good. Jon-Jon was still a problem. He was always trying to hold on to me and didn't want to let go. I was home sleeping one night, and Shon came over after the club. We were both asleep when I suddenly felt someone standing over us. I opened my eyes, wondering if I was dreaming. Jon-Jon was standing there looking like Satan himself. I jumped, and Shon woke up to see Jon-Jon standing there. Shon jumped up, and Jon-Jon rushed him with a brass vase. I was so scared. I took off running out of the house and found somewhere to hide. It appeared Jon-Jon had been drinking and from the look in his eyes, he was drunk. I didn't want to leave Shon, but there was no reason to let him kill us both. A minute or two passed and I saw Jon-Jon leave the house. I ran back into the house to check on Shon. He was okay, but his leg was messed up. Shon's sister let Jon-Jon in, and he acted a damn fool! Once again, he was disrespecting my man and me.

Shon was tired of Jon-Jon hating, and I was tired of Shon cheating and having babies all over the place, so we went our separate ways. We didn't stop having sex because I couldn't get enough of him. The green light was always on for that, but we could no longer be in a relationship.

One day I saw Shon's brother with a cat that I had never seen. The cat was well dressed in slacks, a nice dress shirt, and a fresh pair of Italian leather shoes. Shon's brother knew that his brother was a whore, we had been dating well over a year, and every month he had another girl. I wasn't about to play Shons' game any more so when I saw the opportunity to get at something I liked I moved. I wished it wasn't Shon's brothers' boy, but I liked what I saw, and the game was the game.

He introduced me to him, his name was Rashad. The cat was from K.C. but lived in California he seemed like a real gentleman, he didn't wear jeans he dressed like a businessman, he was a businessman all right, he was a big-time drug dealer. We had started seeing each other when he came to town, I liked him and I knew that if I liked a man that meant that it wasn't going to be a good situation because I only was attracted to men that were not ready for a serious relationship, and had several women. I only liked D-boys and D-boys always ended up being trouble.

Rashad started taking me to California with him I liked him, because he moved different from the cats that I normally dealt with, he was more of a laid-back type player. I had a thing for bad boys, criminals' and drug dealers all together I couldn't shake them, I never tried, later I found out that Rashad would have other chicks from K.C. and other states in town while I was in L.A. Some of them were trafficking drugs for him and some was just cool with him like I was. I didn't traffic drugs for niggas, I was nobody's mule and if a nigga got up the nerve to ask he would get cursed out real fast. I didn't care about what he was doing because I was out their networking with other people. I met another guy from L.A., so I had both and things were going good. They both were giving me what I wanted, money, plus I had my own.

Rashad wasn't giving up cash like the other cat was, I just wasn't asking being prideful. I told any man that I dealt with that I was broke all the time. I didn't care how much money I had, they would give me more. They would always ask me what I was doing with my money. I would tell them I didn't know where it was going, I guess the mall, just give me more. I was saving mine and spending their money, after all what they gave me wasn't shit compared to what I was making on my own, and saving.

I started going to Cali on my own, and I began to meet a lot of important people that helped me make the connections I needed, to help me expand my business. I was about that money and I needed to make it happen. I hollered at my girl Shona in Cali and she hollered at her dude, we started making moves. They started bringing the chronic to Kansas City and that was all she wrote.

I became the chronic lady. I had the whole city on lock with that Cali bud, I was making so much money that I didn't have to sell that white stuff anymore I wanted out, cocaine carried way too much time and I didn't want any parts of the feds. I had two kids and I needed to be there for them, even though I know I could have and should have been a better mother. I started moving ounces and pounds and pounds of weed, I mean a lot. I stop dealing with dudes in my city because I was on to bigger and better things. I was no longer local I was trying to be international, and plus I was too much for the Kansas City, cats now. I was hot and everybody knew it. In the process of me doing my thing my child's dad Jon-Jon went back to federal prison, this time for twenty years. It was so many black men going to federal prison, it was crazy! They were giving them "Buck Rogers" time as E-40 said. Niggas was getting twenty years and up for hard cocaine but the white man that was distributing out the powder was getting a slap on the risk. I wasn't trying to get caught up like Jon-Jon, and Marijuana wasn't going to land you a life sentence like the cocaine might so that's what I was strictly selling, chronic. I knew I had to make it happen for my kids. I started grinding harder and harder. I was getting real money plus I had a lot of cats that had love for me that would help me out, without me having sex with them. It was big brother love; I was the Queen of my city.

Cats in other states would tell dudes about me, they would tell them that I was good people and that I would look out for them when they came to my city. When they got to K.C. we would kick it and get money. Don't get me wrong I was never any one's mule but if they came to my town with their product, best believe I could move whatever it was. I was the man, well the woman, a Boss Chick.

I started traveling going back and forth getting connected with the trees. By this time, I was serving all the cities and surrounding states around me. My crew and I where the female untouchables, everybody wanted us, even though some of the girls had started smoking sherm (that's PCP). Shit some of my crew even smoked crack but the guys didn't care, some of the dudes messed with them just to get next to me thinking I could put them on. I tried to work with a few of them but would end up losing money. They always had a story to tell when they didn't have my cash. Some of the dudes smoked sherm, so I know where the money was going. I would give them a little weed to sell just to try them out; they couldn't even come back with the five hundred dollars they owed me.

I was never down with that smoking other drugs shit but I stayed down with my girls. We all helped each other in different ways; some were boosters, check writers and working girls. We never judged each other if we were getting money we were good. I tried to keep us together, because the other crew I use to roll with fell totally off. Most of them started smoking crack and PCP. Shara was one of the main ones shermed out looking a damn mess! On top of that she became an alcoholic. She had been a fly girl now she was lost and turned out. That's what happens when you go against the grain, plus only the strong survived and I was one of the strong ones.

My cousins Tabby and Vickie moved to K.C., and it was on. They were my favorite cousins and we needed more family around. I was getting money and on a mission. I had met this guy from Cali name Blue; he told me if I ever needed some sherm that he had gallons of it. Blue told me to call him any time. One day I decided to call him and see what he was talking about. It was hard to talk or explain what I wanted, we didn't do much talking on the phone, I learned that from all the cats getting caught up, talking on the phone got most of them in trouble. I asked him could he come and see me. He said he would, he said that I would have to give him a few days and he would be coming through K.C.

I ran around for the next few days with Tabby showing her around and taking her to meet some of my main bud customers. Tabby had worked at the dog pound in Omaha for years and now she was in K.C. She had not found a job yet but she was a hustler so she was going to fit in just fine. When we would leave out from chilling with different cats, Tabby would be laughing telling me that I was too much. I asked her what made her say that. She said because everybody you just sold a sack to smoked half of the sack with you. I laughed and told her to get used to it because that's how it went, we were high and laughing headed to the next spot, Tabby was now a weed smoker. she didn't smoke back in Omaha, now it was going down with her. I got calls all day for that bomb, if they were spending more than one hundred dollars I would deliver it, and help them smoke their sack.

Blue finally arrived into town from "The Land", that's what we called Cali, we talked a little, I asked him about buying some gallons of the sherm. He gave me a reasonable price for the deadly drug, I was anxious to see what my profit was going to be. I knew the profit would be great, after all I wouldn't smoke that shit to save my life! After I smoked it when I was younger and it made me feel demobilized it was out of the question, I knew that it would never go down my lungs again. Rules on the street were, don't get high off your own supply and no one had to worry about me smoking that shit. I started off slow selling a few gallons of sherm and saw a great profit the money was great! The bottles of vanilla flavor were selling like they were in grocery stores. I couldn't believe how many people were on it. The ballers would buy a bottle just to smoke on; the bottles were three hundred and fifty dollars. I was going through ten to fifteen bottles a day. I imagined all the zombies that I had created; it wasn't a good look at all. I was feeling bad about what was going on in my neighborhood, after a while I told myself that I had to quit selling that poison. It had people doing all type of crazy shit.

People were literally going crazy off that shit. They were killing each other and themselves. I would see people get naked and run down the street, kick out windshields; cry like babies, that shit had some bad side effects. Damn, that's the craziest drug that I had ever known to this day. My home girls that were using it would steal bottles from me and lie on each other about stealing it. One day I wouldn't give one of my homeboys a stick to smoke, that's a MORE cigarette dipped in PCP; he called the police and told them that my sister and I was dealing and had gallons of the shit in the house. We did but they didn't react until days later, they kicked in the house and the sherm was gone. So, we had to cut his ass off, he wanted to get high so bad that he snitched on us right in our face. I wasn't that stressed about them kicking in the door because we had two other spots and they were doing big numbers.

I had all females in my crew and we were clocking major paper. I hired this one smoker named Dick; he sold dope on the blocks for cats that had crack houses. Dick liked hanging around all of us ladies; he called us the lady gangster crew. He did everything that I asked him to do and he got paid as well. Much better than what he was getting from the other cats. They might give him twenty dollars and a rock to sit and sell their drugs all day. I showed him love; he left every night with enough money to buy cigarettes, gin, and at least a sixteenth of dope.

He loved his crack, he wasn't feeling the sherm though, and he didn't want to smoke it either so that was good. I didn't have to worry about him stealing from me. His love was for the pipe. I had been going back in forth to L.A. with Rashad, so Dick was good to have around when I was out of town.

Chapter 5
Street Dreams

There was about to be a rap convention in L.A. Rashad asked me to come fly out to Cali and go to the convention with him. He said that flight was leaving that evening, that's what I liked about him the instant gratification. He told me to pay for my ticket, and I would get reimbursed when I got to Cali. I packed and went straight to the airport. When I arrived in L.A., I had my girl Shona pick me up so we could smoke and catch up on what was going on in our lives. I told her that I was going to need to hook up with her man before I left so I could put in my order and he could mail my goods to me. I told her that I would talk to Rashad first and see what he could do for me then I would get back with her, Shona said cool. We went to Roscoe's chicken and waffles and grabbed a bite to eat like we always did. Every time I flew out to L.A. I would go to Roscoe's and have a number nine, which consisted of, three wings and a waffle, and a side of cheese eggs. My beverage was a sunrise; it was a lemonade and iced tea that sat on top of each other, and once you put in the straw it would split apart, I always stressed to execute the prank at home, but never mastered it. After we finished talking and eating, we drove down to Crenshaw and Imperial and met with Rashad at M and M's restaurant.

Rashad and I talked for a bit; he asked me what I had been up to in K.C. I told him that I was pushing sherm. He asked me how that was going. I told him that they loved it down there, and cash was flowing like hell, but niggas were ignorant on it. He said that he could get his hands on some and if I had one of my girls to come out to L.A. that they could test it and see what it was like. I said cool and got right on it.

I called one of the girls in my crew; her name was Poo, she was a hell of a booster, and down for the team. She had started smoking sherm, and it had her messed up. The chicks in the crew that did smoke sherm they wouldn't do it in front of me, or the rest of the ones that didn't get down. I didn't want to see them smoking it either but now I needed her to test it and see would they like it back in the city. Plus, she was going to take a complimentary trip to Cali, while testing out something she liked smoking. I called her and told her that I needed her and that her plane would be leaving out the next morning. I gave her all the flight information, then gave her instructions on where I would pick her up, I told her I would see her soon.

Rashad and I got dressed we met up with his boys and went to the rap convention; it was at the Marriott hotel at LAX and Century Blvd. All the rappers were in the building; Dr. Dre was with Michel'le. Snoop Dog and Tupac were also in attendance; he was still rocking with Thug life. I was having a ball. We were drinking Dom Perignon, and I was feeling and looking good like I was a celebrity myself. Rashad wasn't doing too bad himself. He was fly, and his jewelry was looking better than some of the rappers. Celebrities must have believed he was somebody because they were walking over, shaking his hand.

Chuck D. from Public Enemy walked over and was talking to us like we had been allies for years, I loved every single moment of it, Rashad whispered to me who is he, he looks familiar. I told him that he was the leader of the political rap group, Public Enemy. I told him that they believed he was somebody famous, he was in my eyes, he was my champion and that night I was his, just when everything was going well, I started taking pictures with all of the rappers and Sinbad the comedian, I was going to have some good pictures to take back home and show off I had already gotten Tupac's autograph now I just needed my picture, of us together, but people wanted to get silly, after I took pictures with a few of the rappers like Snoop and Corrupt, I asked one of them to take my picture with Tupac, when I gave them my camera and drink to hold the guy took off and kept both. I went over to Rashad and showed him the cat that took my camera and had the nerves to be sipping on my drink. The cats with Shad were Bloods and was already waiting, for something like this to happen, they said the rappers be on some bullshit and always wanted to try someone. We walked over to where all of Snoop and his posse were, the big homie that was with us took my drink out of the cat with the blue rag around his neck and in his pockets. That's when all hell broke loose. Everyone was fighting, Bloods against Crips. When I say banging, they tore the front foyer of the hotel up. Chairs were being thrown, glass was everywhere, I had run to the side of the room so I wouldn't get hit, I slid almost falling because it was so wet, somehow Snoop was right next to me, and said damn baby girl, see all the confusion you started, I felt I hadn't begun shit, they took what was mine, for no reason at all, but I never wanted anything like that to go down. It had become so bad that security had put us out through the kitchen. I was scared as hell, praying that when we got outside, no one would be waiting, and start shooting, because the guys I was with was strapped, and ready to let loose. The embassy suites where I was staying was right across the street, they dropped me off and said they were going back to kill some crabs. Shad didn't smoke weed, but he made sure that I kept a sack he had his boy give me a fat bag. He took care of me when I was in town; now I was praying that tonight no one would die.

They had stayed out all night, doing what, I didn't want to know. The morning had snuck up on us, Rashad told me to drop him off at the house and go pick Poo up from the airport. I always had a good sense of direction, dating back to when I was a child, so I learned my way around L.A. fast, and I would always drive all around the city. I picked up Poo, and we drove around L.A. for a few hours. Poo was telling me that there had been a double murder back in the city and that the town was on fire. Two of my homeboys that were real cool had been murdered, and their family wanted revenge. I felt so sorry for them and their family, but that's what went on in the town, it was showing no signs of slowing down.

Poo had asked about the good malls out here in L.A.; she was trying to do some shopping. It was a beautiful Saturday a great day to be out, plus we were out of town kicking it in Cali, and it was Valentine's Day. I told her that I wasn't going to the mall with her and that she should chill. She was out here to test the product not go to the mall and steal. I called Shona anyway and told her that my girl was with me and that she was trying to hit the mall up. Shona said that she would like the Del Amo Fashion Center Mall; in Torrance California. She said her cousin goes and hits them up all the time. She told me that they had a lot of security and that Poo had better be careful.

Rashad had found a chick to take Poo to the mall. He told Poo to grab him a couple of outfits, don't get greedy and she would be good. Poo or any of my crew that boosted, didn't charge me for anything; everything I got was in the house. We did things for each other, and that's the relationship we had, so I put my order in. I wanted some stuff out of Victoria's Secret and a couple of outfits out of Marciano because we didn't have it in K.C. The mall was huge, so I knew they would be gone for a while. Rashad was out, so I had Shona pick me up. We went and got manicures and pedicures. I loved getting my hands and feet done when I was in L.A. Because it was so much cheaper than back at home and the Asians took better care of you. After we finished at the nail shop, we headed to Roscoe's chicken and waffles. I could have eaten it twice a day. I ordered my usual a number nine all the time, three wings and a waffle with a side of cheese eggs. I never got a wrong plate when I went to Roscoe's.

Poo had called and said that she had a good day and that she was ready to get drunk. Poo liked to get drunk and would act a damn fool on liquor. We were out of town so what the hell, I told her that we could turn up. I was ready to get loaded myself. I told her that after I finished eating that we would meet back at Rashad's house. Shona and I left the restaurant; she had a date so she dropped me off and told me that she would hook up with me tomorrow. Rashad's house was cracking now, a few guys from St. Louis and Kansas City had popped up. Everybody was handling business; Rashad had two brothers that were in business with him. They were there too; actually, it may have been their house. I watched all the moves being made. These cats had it going on; they had people transporting sherm, cocaine, and weed all over the world. I couldn't believe how people were transporting those drugs around like it wasn't a thing, all for the love of money. I didn't want money that bad; I was good on the transporting, being a mule was not for me.

We all got out that evening; we went to a club called safe sex first, then the Century Club in Hollywood. The club was jumping hard; we were drinking up some liquor, Poo was dancing and had got drunk as hell. She started talking all kinds of shit; all the cats were ready to whoop her ass, no matter how much shit she spoke she was my friend, and I wouldn't let them put their hands on her. We left the club and went to a restaurant, in Englewood, Poo said that she was sick and wanted to lay down in the truck while we finished eating. We all laughed at her drunk ass, as she stumbled to the car. After we finished eating, we headed to the car to go home and get some rest, by this time it was 4 am in the morning, and I was worn out from the night before and tonight. I just wanted to get some sleep, Poo had gotten into the car and locked all the doors with the keys and went to sleep. We had to beat on the windows and shake the car for over an hour. She was so drunk that we had to call someone to come and unlock the door. Rashad was pissed off, I had warned him about Poo's behavior and told them to quit buying her drinks at the club, I said to him welcome to my world, he shook his head, and we drove home.

The next afternoon when Poo woke up I told her how she had us locked out of the car and about her talking crazy to everyone; she couldn't believe that she had cut up as she did. I knew she would say that, but she did it all the time. She apologized and was ready to hit the mall again Rashad told her that he would call the chick to take her, but the chick only had a couple of hours to be out, Poo said she was ready. I told her to run and get right back because I wanted her to smoke some of the wet daddy, to consider how it was. I knew that she would go and come right back, because she had not smoked all weekend, and was ready to get wet.

Rashad dropped me off over in Shona's neighborhood; he was a blood and Shona's hood was seven four hoover Crips.' He would say let me get the hell up out of here before I have to smoke one of these crab ass niggas. I enjoyed hanging out in her hood; it was always something cracking; we would see the police chasing cats down, homies coming through smoking, and a whole lot of family love. I loved her entire family. Every time I came in town they showed me, mad love.

I was sitting on the porch rolling a blunt, when I got a call, it was the Hawthorne police department, they said that Poo had been caught shoplifting at the Eddie Bauer store. The officer said that if we could come now that we could make bail from the jail in the mall, and if not, we would have to go and get her from the county jail. I told him that we would be on our way. I called Rashad and told him what had happened; he said that he would get her and pay the bond. Poo had gone back to the mall for Rashad; he liked Eddie Bauer because he had just bought a brand-new 1995 Eddie Bauer truck. Rashad wanted a jacket that cost five hundred dollars, to floss while he drove the truck and Poo was trying to get it. She would hit the Eddie Bauer store up in K.C. On the plaza, on a regular basis, but the Del Amo wasn't having it. While waiting for Rashad to call, Shona, her cousins and I smoked on some bomb and discussed our next business move on how to get the next batch of chronic back to K.C. Shona said that we should mail it. I was afraid of the mail and preferred that it be driven back. Everyone in the town had been mailing drugs, making it hot. She said that she had a couple of friends that worked at the drop box and that they would make sure that it was packed right and they were for sure that it would make it through. I told her that I would think about it and we could do whatever we were going to do in the morning.

The day had gone by fast, and I had not heard back from Rashad. He had gone and picked Poo up from the mall hours before; I gave him a call to ask him what was going on with Poo. He told me that he had to spend one thousand dollars on her bond and that she was resting because she had an issue when they got back to the house. Rashad asked me if I could have Shona drop me off because he was watching Poo. I said what do you mean you're watching Poo? He said just get over here, and we'll talk. I asked Shona to drop me off, because something was wrong with Poo. I knew that she had drunk a lot the night before, but Poo never had hangovers she could consume some liquor.

Shona drove me back to Englewood. We laughed about Poo always being so drunk. I told her about how Shad's homies that were hanging out with us wanted to fight her because she was so drunk and talking shit to them. I told her how his Cali dudes were tripping, about how Poo was acting saying that their chicks or home girls didn't talk slick to them and how they would usually slap a broad in the mouth for having loose lips. I apologized for Poo and asked them to let it go because it was over before it became a problem. We were there to make money, and we didn't want any problems, all Shona could do is shake her head, saying get her out of here, and get her back to K.C.

Shona dropped me off; I told her that we would hook up in the morning and handle our business, before I boarded my plane. We said our goodbyes, she drove off, leaving me standing there wondering, what in the world had Poo gotten herself into.

Rashad and his home boys were sitting around the table when I walked in the house; everybody was looking at me smiling, mischievously, things couldn't have been that bad by the dirty looks on their faces. I walked over to Rashad asking where was Poo? He responded saying that, she was in the back room getting some rest, because she had fainted earlier. I knew she had drunk a lot of liquor but fainting the next day, which had never happened. Shad told me that after he picked Poo up from the mall, they came back to his house and he let her smoke a stick of the sherm. He said that after she hit it, she had walked out the back door, like a mummy, and sat on the swing, after about ten minutes he said that he went out to check on her, she was laid out on the ground unconscious. Rashad said that they had to call the ambulance and everything, he said at first; he thought she was dead and was thinking where would they throw, or bury her body. I couldn't believe what I was hearing. I was fucking with some heartless Niggas, that would do what they had to do to cover their ass. I said to Rashad "the shit is that potent"? You're going to kill somebody, he said, I told you it was no joke! If that's what they want let's give it to them.

I went to the back room to check on Poo; she was trying to come back to life, looking delirious. She saw me and said, girl that shit was so fire that I passed out, I saw my life pass before my eyes, I think I saw the devil. She said all I can remember was waking up, and all these white people were surrounding me. The white people were the paramedics, coming to get her crazy ass. She stated they called for her blood pressure and temperature, they asked her did she recognize her name, and where she was? She answered those questions, they had no other option but to leave her there with the drug dealers, that had almost taken her life, with that deadly ass drug, it sounded scary to me as she explained about her out of body experience, especially the part of dying and seeing the devil! But now it was funny, only because she was ok. I asked her should I grab a few gallons of the drug. She said most definitely. That was all she wrote. I wondered how someone would want to smoke something that paralyzed them. I just didn't get it, but if she liked it, I knew the wet heads in the town would love it, I shouldn't have even wanted to sell something that was so crazy, but for the love of money, it was about to go down.

Chapter 6
Shermed Out; For the Love of Money

We were back in the city waiting for the sherm to arrive I told Tabby, Charlie, and Dick what happened with Poo out in Cali, she was laughing with us as well. They asked me did Poo behave herself in Cali. I told them about her almost getting her ass kicked by the dudes with Rashad, and how she locked us out of the truck. Poo was a mess, but overall, we had a good time.

I told them that the town is going to love us. Dick said that he was ready to make that money and that he would work every day. He was a hell of a worker and would make that money for you. I attempted to bring Dick to stop smoking crack. I told him to imagine how much money he could have if he weren't hitting the pipe, but if he kept my money right, there was not much I could do. With me he would make, at least eight hundred dollars a week, Dick said he was cool, and he was going to smoke crack until he died. I just bit my tongue and let it go. I let him work because he would stay up all night. I didn't work nights, that's when I would shut down the place, but nighttime was when all the zombies were ready to fume. They were going about looking like they were in the Michael Jackson video Thriller.

The PCP had arrived on Wednesday, and it was time to find out what the town thought about it. I already had fifty bottles sold before they even arrived. The vanilla flavor bottles were three hundred and fifty dollars apiece; the More cigarettes were twenty dollars apiece, we also had fifty-dollar valves. I had a great plug on the gallons, they were going for eleven thousand in my city, and I was getting them for six thousand doubling my profit.

For the following weeks, we ran hard with the sherm. I was dipping twenty-dollar sticks, to selling vanilla flavor bottles. The city was now, worse than what it had been. I was getting money, but it wasn't good money because everybody was so scary looking, they were all losing weight, they were making hater moves, Money was coming fast, but lives were being taken away. I came home one day and had left Poo to watch all four kids, she was sleeping when we went away, once we came back home, I walked in, Angel ran to the door, she said mommy Poo is in the room and she's holding up the wall, because she said it's going to fall. Did you say holding up the wall? Baby, what do you mean? I asked out of curiosity? She said she's holding it, see, she grabbed my hand guiding me towards the room. I went in to see what was going on with Poo, and there she was standing on the wall holding it up or so she thought, saying that it was going to fall. I was mortified by her behavior, in front of my daughter, nieces, and nephews. I pulled her off the wall and told her that she better not ever smoke that shit while she was around our kids again. Trecie wanted to kick her ass, but Charlie wouldn't let her, plus Poo was higher than a kite. All I could do was shake my head. I was blameworthy because I was the one feeding the town with it, and she had easy access. She was gone on that shit, but she was our girl, we had, to try and help her or deal with her. She was as sweet as can be when she was sober. She just had a problem, and it was the PCP.

Two weeks had gone by, and the sherm was just about gone, I had made a lot of money on the treacherous drug. I was ready to get more, but I wanted to wait a week or so. The major difference between selling the sherm and the weed was that the chronic smokers were calm with no problems and the sherm smokers were crazy and would rob you if they had an opportunity... They had sob stories and couldn't think straight; you would have to watch your back because they would rob your ass in a New York minute. We were always strapped and ready for whatever. That was the nature of the beast, and you could never be caught slipping.

It was Friday the 13th the girls and I were seated at the spot on 39th and Brooklyn. Poo was telling us how her brother had got murdered on

Friday the 13th. She stated that she hated this day and that she only wanted to lay down, which was a serious thing for Poo, a detox day. She told us how Shara's brother and cousin had killed her brother on his birthday; it was so sad how she talked about what they had done to him I hugged her and told her I felt her pain. I told the girls that we were going to turn in early anyway. We experienced an event earlier that day with one of the youngsters that were always two doors up from the spot, about a stick of sherm that he had purchased; he was high out of his mind talking out the side of his neck. He wanted a free stick and wasn't about to get it. Wet heads were always trying to find a way to get over, for their next strike! He articulated that he didn't get his full twenty dollars' worth and he needed another single. He was looking crazy, and vindictive as fuck. He spooked us out, with the menacing look that was on his face. That made me shut down the operation and go home for the night and chill, better safe than sorry. Dick didn't want to go home. I told him that I would drop him off on 45th and Chestnut, where he hung out, and we called, the block because we were heading home for the night. We were out of product, so there was no reason to stay there. Everyone was going home. We were always out of there before ten o clock. I didn't want to go out because it was Friday the 13th. I wasn't superstitious, but even when it wasn't Friday the 13th there would be shooting somewhere in the town; it was already a murder a couple of times a week. With it being Friday the 13th somebody was almost definitely going to get lit up in Killa City. Precisely because of the date some cat would start an ignorant ass fight and make the murder rate go higher.

Around midnight I got a call from the chick that lived up the street from the spot. I had given her my number for when she saw strange activity going on at the spot, such as a kick in or robbery, I wasn't prepared for what she was about to tell me. She spoke with a tremble in her voice. She was probably high, she was another one that loved those sherm sticks, she looked out for me, and I took care of her. She told me that there were police all around the house. She asked were we ok? I told her, yes; we were at home in the bed. There were no drugs in the house either so what were they doing. The chick said it looked like a kick in. I told her to walk past the house and see what was going on and to call me back as soon as she found out. I leaped up and told Charlie and Trecie what was going on and that the chick up the street was going to ring back after she walked past the spot to investigate. Trecie rolled a blunt, we smoked and waited for our call. The phone rang it was the chick. She had a different tone now, and it was like I could hear her heart beating through the phone. I asked her what in the world had happened. She said that there had been a homicide and a man was in the house. I dropped my head, knowing that it was Dick. He was the only one that didn't leave, I told him to go, but he wanted to stick around. I felt tormented, I didn't know his family or anything, and here it was all because of the potent drug that I was selling, another life had been taken away. The following morning the police were picking me up and interviewing me. Dick in the hand as we called him, had driven my car home the day before to his mom's house, that's why they were questioning me. The police interrogated me asking various questions about why was he in my car before the slaying. They asked about the house; they also asked where I was at the time that he was murdered. Thank God, we were all at home lounging because it might have been one of us, a matter of fact it could have been all of us. I don't know who could have murdered Dick. The only person I could think of was the sherm head from earlier in the day that was thirsty for a stick, and when he didn't get it, he decided to rob us. The crazy part was he was Shon's stepbrother, but what did that mean, shit he was jealous of him and probably plotting to rob him when the opportunity came. I was questioned and let go. It was so messed up that whoever it was killed Dick, the police said that he was sitting in a chair asleep when he was shot and robbed. They couldn't have taken much out of the house because we were out of sherm before we had even left the house that evening. Dick probably only had fifty dollars in his pocket no drugs and his crack pipe. We had to stop selling sherm because it was getting to be a curse. I had told Shon about the robbery, and I felt that his brother had murdered Dick. He said that he didn't deal with him at all and it sounds like something he would do. I and Shon always stayed cool. He was just about the only man that could get in my pants at any time he wanted, I had that come back pussy, and he had that come back dick, I didn't care who he was with we would always fuck.

A few weeks after Dick was murdered shit hit the fan with that sherm. I sat and observed everybody that was getting wet; it had everybody out of their element. I saw some of my best chronic buyers and some of the best hustlers that we had in town now gone off it. My Godson, little Dave's daddy, had been smoking for a while and got turned out; he had got so out of control that he killed himself with a shotgun, blowing his brains out, weeks after Dick was murdered. People on sherm always wanted to kill someone or themselves. Who would even want to be on something that made you want to harm yourself? I just didn't get it but knew I would have to either keep being greedy selling it or let go and save my friends as much as I could, they could get it anyway, but I didn't want it to be from me. PCP was now taking over the town, and I knew for sure that, I had to stop selling it. My best friend J.C. had even started smoking it. I tried to keep selling it, but by now it had taken over the city and our neighborhood in a horrible way. Restaurants had begun to close because no one was eating, it was Zombie Land. I couldn't keep feeding that shit to my people. Don't get me wrong; they were still going to get it just not from me anymore.

I wished that everyone who was selling would only quit after all we were feeding the city poison; the town was like the movie night of the living dead. I gained a large lot of money selling PCP, but I said to myself that no matter how tough it got, or I was doing I wouldn't sell it anymore. I could have gotten it for free, and I still wouldn't have sold it. I was retired from the sherm game and was back on to what I did best, selling weed, and I guess I can say my body. I believed I was tricking Cats out of their money, but as they say, a fair exchange was no robbery, and even though I had sex with only the ones I held some interest, in, I was still a woman of the street, better yet a hoe. I hooked up with a friend of mine, who was just like my Big brother, King kept good weed and had bricks. People would say why do you hang with him, he robs, and kills people? In my eyes, he wasn't like everyone said he was, plus, he never tried to rob me or anyone I recognized. He was a damn good person and still is. He was a real boss playa and put me up on a lot of game; he also wouldn't let anyone mess with me, The Queen Bee.

Chapter 7
Playing the game

Big Scooter was another one of my close homies who had all the connections on the chronic. I kept my links tight on the weed always. Marijuana sold better than anything with little to no chance of going to Federal Prison. Cash was getting short, I was spending money, but not bringing any in, but it felt right to give up selling sherm then to ruin another life. Greed would get you killed or locked up. Scooter connected me with a couple of pounds of some purple Cush; I made sure that it was dismissed. He said it was from Humboldt County, I knew that the weed that came from Northern California was always the best. I got my clientele back to the weed, well, I never lost them. I was again making paper, but I needed more than two pounds. If I bought it for five thousand dollars, and only arrived at three thousand, net, I wasn't gaining ground, plus what I smoked. I would sell the pounds in a workweek. I needed enough to last at least a month, and to get my weight back up. That meant I would have to go to Cali and get it myself; I had plugs to get it, now I would have to find someone to bring it back for me. Scooters' connect was cool, but the cost was inflated once it came back to K.C. I needed to cut out the middleman; I wanted Cali prices, that way I could at least come home with five pounds. I started going to St. Louis. The cats in the Lou as we called it, wasn't smoking chronic like we were in Kansas City. They were still getting their clothes burned by seedy weed. Our city was turned out on all types of exotic weed. There was a select few in St. Louis that smoked chronic but I was about to get it in and hook the whole city up, of course, the D-boys would be my main target.

I would hit up the barber shops in the Lou and let them try it out. St. Louis barber shops were like the club. I mainly went to this one barbershop off 70 East and Natural Bridge Hwy. It was called Grips. It was a car wash, beauty salon and barber shop. We met all kinds of people there. I was riding clean in my, burgundy J30, Infinity with the leather peanut butter seats. I could get the bugs washed off from being on the road trip. When you came to Grips, it was a one-stop shop. You could get a car wash, get chosen by a major player in the town, or choose up. Russie had already had my hair looking fly. My focus was selling bud and finding connections on whatever else I could hustle up on. That was my kind of spot. Some of the guys said that the weed was way too expensive, so I took taste testers, for them to try it out, after smelling the sweet aroma they wanted to see what this exotic marijuana was about. One hit was all it took, most of the cats that said that it was too expensive had started smoking it, after a couple of trips back in the fourth they had gotten addicted and had to have it. I also was making trips to Omaha, Nebraska. They were already up on the chronic because the Cali cats were there flooding the small town with every drug possible. I had seven grams for two hundred-fifty bucks. I was breaking pounds down making straight paper if hadn't been smoking I could have cleared fifteen thousand on each pound.

I stayed on the road for myself, networking. Never would I transport drugs for anyone else. If I were going to Prison, it would be for me, and I wouldn't have to rat anyone out. When I would go to STL, I would always meet important people in the circle that I was in they were considered big fish, some whales. I always went to the best clubs in the city to see what was popping. Guys would try to get at me, but I was on a mission looking for cats that wanted Weed. When I had my mind on money, a nigga was the last thing I was thinking about. I fed them the cold shoulder, exactly like they did us chicks. I had my mind on my money and my money on my mind. I went to a club called Plush; it was off the chain. Everybody was partying and doing their thing, a few cats came over and tried to holler at Charlie, her ass was fat, waist small, plus she was chocolate with a flawless complexion, making men want to step to her. They asked what we were doing after the club; she told them that we were going to grab some white castle and head back to the hotel room, by the River front to get some rest.

The guys asked her, did we want to get some fast money. Charlie told them that we were constantly attempting to get money. She asked them, what did they have in mind, making money. The guy told her that he and his boys wanted to compensate us for sex, that we'd received a couple of thousands, depending on what sex acts we performed. She laughed at him, offended, saying we don't sell pussy do we look like hoes or something? I thought it was degrading that they had even stepped to her like that, it was all good because we ended up selling them a couple of ounces anyway. That was fast money in my book.

The following day we headed back to Grips car wash, I wanted to tally out the scene and make at least a quick thousand, and check out the scenery. We ran across some baller cats at the car wash, when they jumped out of the black Dooley truck, they smelled the bomb coming out of my car, asking where did we get it from? I told them that we got it from us, and had it right here on the deck. They asked where were we from because they knew that we weren't from anywhere around St. Louis, as close as the cities was, we had totally different looks, even the gold teeth in our mouth was different, in my eyes Kansas City gold looked better, the gold was shiny, we rocked diamonds in our teeth too. St. Louis people golds, looked like copper pennies. I let the main cat that was asking all the questions and driving the truck hit the blunt, and immediately he bought a sack, this started a lifelong relationship. His name was Chad. He would become one of my dearest friends and my brother, we would be, and are family four life. He was a straight boss, super fly, with a fat bald head. He was laid back, and always calm, his crew was fly as well, every one of them had big nice cars and trucks, I was riding clean, but nothing like the Dirty boys in the Lou. After we sat around and smoked, we headed back down to the embassy suites by the river front. It became a weekly thing, if I weren't in St. Louis, they would come to K.C. We kicked it hard, and smoked like chiefs; they smoked just like I did.

I was moving pounds, but I could smoke an ounce or two in one day. I was a true go-getter. I also sold dinners, I was a top chef, without going to culinary school, the skills I adopted from my mother, grandmother, and aunts, I was a beast in the kitchen, but couldn't keep a man. What was I doing wrong?

When Chad and his boys started coming in town they could stop through and not only get ounces or pounds of weed but eat good free of charge; we were a family now. They would buy their weed, eat a meal, then smoke it up with the girls and me, before they left they would have to buy another, sack to go. I made good money but spent just as much; managing money was not right for me. I liked to splurge, not thinking about laying aside for a rainy day as I had started in the beginning. I was thinking of the moment person,

After that evening of hanging out in the Lou with the dirty boys, me, Charlie, and Tabby went to the skating rink, while we were still in STL we said that we might as well hit up the rink, because they partied at the rink as we did back in my town. The weekend was just roughly over, it was Sunday night, and we were going to be headed home. I came across this guy named Skooter. He appeared so innocent and sweet as they say don't let the look fool you. He was a heavy hitter. He wasn't innocent at all, and I knew that because if he was attempting to come at me, I knew that something had to be up, the only men I seemed to attract were bad boys or drug dealers. I didn't know what it was about me, but that's how it was, and I didn't have a problem with it. He called me over to a brand new bright red Tahoe SUV; red was my favorite color, I liked his truck, and was thinking he could be someone that I could add to my little flock. He asked me where I was from? I stated to him, how did you recognize that I wasn't from St. Louis? He said because of your style, and your accent, I know that you're not from around here. He was so St. Louis, he continued saying, "and now that I hear you talk yo accent, it's a dead giveaway." Nor was my hair like the STL chicks, he was checking me out. It did seem like all the chicks in STL rocked the same hair style. We just didn't roll like that; I and my girls were different we rocked all different kinds of hair styles. Our weaves were banging all the time, and the ones that wore short haircuts, kept it fly. He told me if I ever needed anything to just ask, I was mixed up because men usually don't say things like that to you when you first meet them. He said it, and he meant every word of it. I took him up on his offer, and it was all good. We became allies, we talked on the telephone from time to time, he wasn't a phone type of guy, but we kept in contact. I started asking Skooter for things just to find out if he would give it to me. The sky was the limit with Skooter. In return for him being so generous to me, I turned him on to my home boy King. King would connect him with what he needed. Whatever business he did with King he would kick me out a nice amount of cash, without touching or driving drugs around; I received a thousand dollars or better each time.

Skooter and I had never slept together, but I loved him like he was my man. It was hard to find a man that would look out for you, like he did without any strings attached, especially without giving up some ass. Which I realized there were strings attached, I was the plug, the middleman, and could have received as much time as they would if we were ever caught.

I had found him and planned to keep him close by. I would go to STL for concerts, and Skooter would have the tickets and the keys to a luxury suite waiting on me. I was living and loving life, balling and most of all just being me, The Queen.

By now I was well known not only in Kansas City, but in multiple states hustling, and making paper. After a few months of dealing with my St. Louis cats, a guy from Bakers Field California showed up in my town. Someone must have turned him onto K.C., west coast cats new that the Midwest was the place to be for the drug trade. He was setting up shop with some of the best bud that I had tasted in a long time. I was getting my bud from L.A.; he had bay area bud, Northern

Lights, and he had lots of it! I was in love with the taste, of the weed he had brought into the town. I told myself that I had to meet him and get in where I fit in. He had all types of Cush, purple, orange, hell he had different flavors of weed for every day of the week. He was friends with my homeboy Keith; his name was Mac. I told my homeboy Keith to hook me up with him. Keith didn't want to make the connection because he knew how I rolled. He knew I was going to become cool with Mac and he didn't want Mac to become my contact, because it would take away from his money, he had to know that there was enough money to be made without stepping on anyone's toes, after all the whole city was smoking and we all had our clientele. Keith was doing a little hating and wouldn't introduce me because Mac had put him down and he had that bud. I had some good weed, but I was getting my personal sacks from Keith. The weed that they had was so bomb, I always wanted and needed to smoke the best. I was purchasing the Northern Lights from Keith. When Keith wouldn't introduce me to Mac, I took it upon myself to present myself. One night we were in Niecy Lounge on Blue Pkwy when Mac and his boys walked in. They were a cocky crew; I liked how they moved. I took a shot of my Remy Martin VSOP and proceeded over to the bar where they were; I introduce myself to Mac. He knew who I was because he would see me at Keith's and one time I had gone and got him Gates BBQ. If you came to Kansas City, you had to eat Gates. Keith would never introduce us, even though we would be in the Same room, but things were about to change. I walked over to Mac to speak to him; I asked him did he remember me from Keith's place? He said of course he did; he said you pulled up a lot, I then asked him what was he smoking on. He said that he had some purple Cush; and after he got his drink that we could go outside and light up a fat one. That was all she wrote I was in. Keith didn't have to do a thing; I was in!

Chapter 8
The Chronic Explosion

Mac and I instantly clicked. We had the best brother and sister team that anyone could ever conceive of. He had chronic by the truck loads; it was crazy. We had Cush for months because of how it was grown seasonally; Mac had an endless supply. Everyone in the crew was eating off what Mac had brought to the table, but with more money, came more problems. I had more bitches that hated on me and my click, for no reason, but we all knew how to get money. All they had to do was follow suit; it was enough money for everyone in the game. No matter how much money I made the flyer I became. Guess turned into Gucci, and Louis Vuitton. DKNY turned in to Donna Karen and so on. I was still hood, and, would smack a broad quick. Mac would say yawl is some gangsters.

One day my homegirl, Tracy called and told me some chicks wouldn't let her out the house where she was. It was our homeboy Lou's home, but it was in Tracy's name. His sisters were tripping and hating, telling her if she walked outside that they were all going to jump her, Tracy was a banger and would take them all if she had too, and whoop most of their asses all alone. But who wanted to be jumped by five or half a dozen birds. I told her that we were on our way. We loaded up and headed out south. When we got there, we ended up fighting six chicks. Whooping their ass right in front of their brothers, and homies, they started it, and we damn sure finished it. After the battle, we jumped in the car and had to get to the hospital, Charlie had hit my cousin Bunny in the head with a baseball bat, trying to hit one of the birds that we were banging with, we were crazy as hell, not even thinking, she could have killed someone with the aluminum bat. The next day the police detectives came to my house while I wasn't home, they towed my car away, and wouldn't give it back until Tracy and I came and talked to them. Once we finally decided to see what they were talking about so I could get my car, they showed us pictures of one of the chicks, then showed us pictures of her hand. What we didn't know was that one of the chicks that we were fighting, the finger had got cut off, with some knife, as the investigator puts it. I became a damn detective; well she must have managed it herself, they did have weapons, we didn't own any weapons. That was my story, and I was sticking to it. I knew Tracy was in the other interrogation room looking just as surprised as I was after we were interrogated, we figured out when it happened. She had run up on one of us, and in the process, she got her finger sawed off, with a steak knife. Broads had it bad when they stepped to us; we didn't care how tough that they thought their crew was, we felt, that we were tougher, and bossier... We didn't get charged for the assaults, thank goodness that the house was in Tracy name, and if she wanted to, she could have switched the whole situation on them and had everyone locked up, but that's not how we rolled. I was back on my mission, on the grind getting money, fighting was starting to be too much, selling drugs, and kicking it with the chosen few cats, that I thought was worthy of my time, was a much better direction. I considered myself a real hustler. No one could block off my hustle; In my eyes and others, I was considered a Gangster Bitch. Through it all I stayed prayed up, I regularly went to church. I took care of everyone around me, and my girls took care of me. Most of my crew was boosters they would go in a store and come out with trash bags full of merchandise. I tried stealing a few times; I nearly got caught one time, in lame, J.C. Penny's after that happened I left it alone. I was better at hustling drugs. Our children had so much gear you never would see them in the same outfit we were on fleek, how would it have looked if our kids weren't.

Little B's father and his wife were keeping my son away from me, by lying and telling him that I was a bad person and not a good mother. I was never a bad person; or mother, I recognize that I could have been more serious with parenting, but I was young and stupid. I realized that Little B's father was a consistent and secure place because he never sold drugs or carried guns he was the perfect gentleman to raise a young man. What I didn't know was that he would use it against me by not letting me see my son, sometimes a whole year would go by, I could have fought harder to get him, but my lifestyle had me on the go.

My heart was genuine, and I loved the Lord. My whole family was evangelist and Pastors, so I was also covered by the blood of Jesus. I never disrespected my mother, father, or my elders. I only needed to be a better parent; it was time to bring myself together and be the parent that my kids would treasure.

Train a child in the way he should go, and when he is old, he will not depart from it. (Proverbs 22:6)

Family and respect should always come first!

1994-97

My Cali brother Mac and I had been kicking it hard by now. He had the best Cush around the tri-city area, we were stocked up and stacking paper for months on in. I would get six pounds of chronic a month from Mac for myself at four thousand dollars per pound, and sell a few of his pounds as well to make extra side money. Half a dozen pounds, may not sound like a bunch of weed, but when you could earn a seven-thousand-dollar net income off each pound, that was pretty, damn good. Practice the numbers. I was the Cush Lady if they wanted the bomb you had to see me or go through someone to get to me. Tabby, Vickie and I would go to Mac's spot and chill on slow days. We smoked and laughed at Mac's crew. He came to K.C. with a click of his own. They were doing their thing as well, connecting with people and running around from state to state. We always left Mac's spot high as a kite, Mac had smoked us out, and we took in the munchies. We would go to eat at Gates BBQ on 12th street. We ordered a mixed plate, which consisted of, turkey, beef, and, beef sausage. We sat there laughing and eating. We were eating like savages, on the mixed plates, and those thick hot fries that they sold, my eyes were so low that they looked closed, the food would wake me up, and make me want to smoke more, because I would be too full, and always needed a blunt, or two after I ate. We talked about a few cats that walked in ordering food that we knew. Out of nowhere came this young cat; he walked up to the table and said damn tuts I want to feel like you are feeling. I asked him what did he mean, and how did he think I was feeling? He said you high as hell! I was sitting over in the bar when yawl walked in, and the aroma came in with you, and I want some of that. I looked at my girls all we could do was laugh. He told the man I'm for real I'm trying to get some now. I asked him was he the police, he said you got me fucked up, do I look like a policeman, I'm a gangster. Now let me get me some of that what yawl smoking on, I'll show you the police alright tuts. I could see the print in his pants where he had a big gun was on his hip, I asked him what made him think that I had weed, he replied telling me that he knew who I was and had seen me on several occasions, plus a few of his friends dealt with me. I had to be sarcastic asking him, if I sell you some weed, you're not going to rob me with that big gun that's on your hip, he looked down at the bulge sticking out of his shirt, saying I have a bigger gun in my pants that I'd like to rob you with, looking mischievous. He said we met a few weeks ago, at the Inferno, it came right to me, he was the cat that Poo said she wanted to get at, but he was telling me to come here, at the same time. It wasn't looking well for her at that present moment; now he was flirting.

I asked him how much weed was he looking for? He stated that he would get an ounce. I played like I had to call to get it but really had it on me. I kept an ounce broke down into seven grams always, if I were ever stopped, it would be no problem to put it up inside of me. I thought, I would drive around the corner and put it all in one bag, and sell it to him. I told him that he would have to wait about fifteen minutes, he gave me his number and said that he would meet me wherever he had to, to get his goods. We all got up and left. Tabby said little dude must got some cash buying chronic like that. I was like he looks like he's working with something, he was young, but he was fly, he carried himself, like an older cat. Gangster was written all over his face. He had on some fly Polo gear that I hadn't seen around our malls, and his leather Polo boots were on point with his outfit. He was groomed nice and smelling good. A good smelling man was a turn on for me, plus he was about to spend eight hundred bucks for the bomb. His name was Jason. Once I got to know him, I called him Anthony, that's a whole other story. I met back up with him, gave him his bag, and got my money. While I was counting it, he asked me could I get a hold of this all the time, then said, well, I know you can, you're the Chronic Lady, I know more about you than you imagine. I played his response off, telling him whenever, he wanted more, just hit me up. He said ok I'll call, but that's not all I'm going to be calling for. I laughed and told him to stop flirting, even though I liked it. He said, I'm not only flirting, but I'm also laying down my foundation, you'll see, I guess that meant he was going to have me, and somehow, he did. Anthony was the craziest but the coolest young cat that you would ever want to meet. He was a lot younger than me, but he was getting money, and I was on him, like white on rice. He was a sexy chocolate gangster. He was calm but crazy; he had that bag.

Tracy and I would call him Anthony because we use to watch an episode of the Twilight Zone, the little boy on there was named Anthony, and he would make people disappear. My Anthony could be bad and do something like that. I asked someone about him, and they said he is a fool, that didn't take any shit, and he would terrorize anyone that he thought crossed him. Sounded like the boy on the Twilight Zone to me. I would chill with Jason to see what he was about. He was super cool and romantic to be young. He wasn't immature at all he had his shit together, plus he was on some grown man shit. Anthony and I had been hanging out for a few months. Angel loved him because he gave her anything that she wanted. She called him her boyfriend he was real cool with my crew too, when he wasn't acting a fool. If everyone in the crew got a good vibe from a cat it was all good because that didn't happen very often, somebody in our crew always disapproved of one of our men. Anthony had thumbs up with them all. He gave me everything I wanted all the time. He smoked more weed than I did, he would tell me all the time that he could smoke up Jamaica. He said most of the chicks he knew smoked, but they didn't smoke around guys. I told him those chicks were closet smokers like crack heads. I told him that I wasn't concealing anything from anybody and a man would have to deal with it or be gone. I didn't care what a man thought of me; I was going to smoke and do it right in their face. I didn't have a ring on my finger. I was married to the game! He laughed and said tuts that's why a like you, you're real and don't bite your tongue, not even for Daddy.

Anthony was cool, but sometimes he would come around drunk and be looking mean and crazy like he was going to kill someone, shit we knew how he rolled and didn't want to push his buttons, I had a passion for gangsters, and wasn't trying to let him go. We started traveling and doing things together. On Valentine's Day, all his boys and my whole click went to Houston's restaurant, in Kansas on ninety-fifth and Quivira Rd. The staff knew Anthony so they let us stay and party after they closing. We popped several bottles of Dom Perignon, and feasted on a Hawaiian rib eye. Every appetizer that Houston's sold was on the table. Anthony and his boys spent two thousand quickly in that spot. Anthony was fun and exciting, and to be so young, he was getting that paper. We had it going on. We had been kicking it for about seven months. He asked me to go to Vegas with him to the Riddick Bowe vs. Evander Holyfield fight so I said I would go and started packing my bags. The trip was a week away, but I was excited, I started packing early. I didn't pack much because I knew that we would be doing a lot of shopping. Anthony handled everything, I didn't have to make any reservations, just be ready when it was time to move. I got out in the streets all week and made money for my trip. My Boo was taking care of everything but I still rolled with my own cash everywhere I went. I knew chicks that would go out of town with the guys and get left at hotels and never see the guy again. They would have no money to get home, looking crazy as hell. I always thought what kind of chicks are those that gave up their goods, couldn't get back home hell couldn't even get a pack of cigarettes. Those were bum bitches in my eyes that was never going to happen to me because I had my own. If he didn't want to buy me something I would buy it myself, the weekend finally came we were going to be leaving that evening on the last flight out. Anthony called and asked was I packed? I told him that I had packed days ago, and was ready to roll out, he laughed, saying we're going to have a ball tuts, and I'm going to fuck you all over the hotel room, he said that I had never given him head and he wanted me to suck his dick. In his own words, I want you to suck my dick while I'm laid back smoking a blunt, I want you to show me how much you care about me. I was fine with that; our sex life was dope! I was always satisfied with his loving. Even though I wasn't into giving men head, Jason would for sure be one that would get treated. We were talking freaky, and I couldn't wait to get there. Anthony's boy was going also and had gotten into it with the chick that he was taking about two hours before we were leaving, Anthony told me that his boy, Big Head wanted to take someone with him. He said that Big Head had found out some bad things about the girl and wasn't trying to have her at the fight with him. I felt sorry for whoever she was, she was for sure about to miss out on the fun, and I was about to replace her with one of my girls. Anthony asked me did I have one of my girls that Big Head could take. I told him yes and that we would be ready when they came. I ran down stairs and told Tabby to get ready because she was going to Vegas with me. She said you're leaving now, what are you talking about. I told her and so are you, you know how we do. While she was packing, I told her what had gone down with Big Head and his chick, she said what if I don't like him? I said who cares after Vegas you never have to say shit to him again we're about play hard ball. I told her that she would meet her blind date when they picked us up to go to the airport. She laughed and said you are something else Queen, let me finish packing my bags.

Tabby had no kids so she could jump up and leave whenever she wanted to. They came by to pick us up; Tabby was about to meet her blind date. We introduced Tabby and Big Head and headed to the airport. Anthony asked me to stash his weed so that we could have some when we landed. I already had my own, so now I would be stuffing two ounces of weed up in my pussy. I stuffed the weed, and we were on our way. Once we arrived, we went to our room that came with the airline package. It wasn't on the strip. It was downtown with the older hotels. It was a disaster; cats were selling drugs in front of the hotel. Downtown Vegas, was burnt out, we wanted to be on the strip plus we didn't want to see people selling drugs outside the hotel, and Jason wouldn't be getting any of my bomb head if I had to stay there. I wouldn't have been able to concentrate... We left our city for a vacation and to get away from the drug scene for a minute. There was no way we were staying there. We found rooms on the strip and started spending money. We blew over thirty thousand dollars in a few days. We ate, shopped, and smoked like hell. Anthony bought me my first Chanel bag, it was eight hundred dollars, and I was doing my thing, walking around stunting, he was the Man! We went to the fight; Holyfield won, and after the fight, it was on. The club we went to was off the chain we partied with all the stars and had their attention as well. Cats were checking for me, Tabby, and Jason's sister Val; we were coupled up and cool with who we came with. After a few days, Anthony and Big Head had to get back to the city. He asked me did we want to stay; he said that he needed to get back and handle some things. I said, of course, I wanted to stay and finish having fun, Anthony gave me a few more thousands, and we stayed a few more days. While we were hanging out at the MGM, I ran across one of the Cali guys that I had met back in K.C. We had run out of weed; he took us to get more. We hung out with him and talked a little business and went on our way. I had the time of my life.

I returned home to K.C. and was back on my grind. Anthony was the sweetest boyfriend that I had ever had, or whatever he was because he had other women, but I was the one in the spotlight. He always helped me out and never threw anything up in my face. On one occasion, he gave me some cash to go to Cali to re-up on some bud. On the way, back I wrecked out on the freeway with the bud, only to find out that my folks that put the weed in the stash spot for me had stolen it back out when I went to the bathroom. I thought we were cool, but evidently, we weren't. The game is dirty, and you just had to deal with what was coming to you, sometimes you win, sometimes you lose. Anthony put me, Tracy and my friend Shona on a plane. He said baby; it's going to be okay, just come on home, be glad you're alive, shit if you would have died, I wouldn't ever be able to get my dick sucked like you sucked it in Vegas. I need you to kiss on it, and I'll take care of you… he knew how to lift my spirits even though I had lost ten thousand dollars. We went home injured and scratched up really bad. Shona had a neck brace on because she wasn't wearing her seat belt, she was messed up the most, but we were all alive.

I told Mac what had happened to my weed and that I needed bud, but no add-on, on the price, I wanted Cali prices. He liked that because he would hook me up and if I sold out before he did, I would help him sell his weed.

Mac had started hanging out with some guys in the town that I wasn't comfortable with for some reason, and I wasn't seeing him as much. You should always follow your first mind. He was kicking it and giving everyone work, he never let me know he was selling other drugs but others told me, that he was the man, and cats were getting birds from him. I stuck to what we did, weed, because, whatever else wasn't my business and I wasn't trying to mess with that white stuff again, fuck federal prison, I had enough people that were in there and several going. I hooked Mac up with Anthony because he smoked so much that he could get a better deal from Mac. I was breaking my weed down to get more money.

Mac and Anthony were cool, but Anthony was crazy and young and getting a lot of money. That made him stubborn and hardheaded. Mac would try and give him good advice, and feedback to slow down. Anthony said he was listening but he wasn't because he thought he knew it all, he was young and struggled with humility. I was with Anthony all the time. Tracy had started talking to Anthony's friend Budda. Budda wasn't crazy like Anthony, but he was an arrogant asshole and talked a lot of bullshit that no one wanted to hear. He bragged about what he had and how well he dressed, and how he could fuck any bitch he wanted, which was true around town, hoes were thirsty for boss niggas and they had a bossy crew. He also tried to flirt on the sly, but he knew that we didn't move like that. Once you were in our immediate circle that would be it. We didn't share or switch up with men, we had a code, and we stuck to it.

I shared my man once before with someone that I had hung around with, not by choice, and that was with Shara. I said that it would never happen again, our crew was loyal to one another and down, so we didn't trade men, and never worried about one another lurking.

Anthony's homeboy Big Head was just as crazy as Anthony, or crazier; he may have egged Anthony on to do some of the things he did, they were getting money but always getting picked up for murders. I had even been picked up and questioned, for a murder that the police were investigating. Big Head was down for whatever, he was older than Anthony, and a straight nut.

Cats knew not to fuck with them period. They had both just beaten a murder case, making them feel invincible. I had hooked my cousin Tabby up with Big Head when we went to Vegas, and they hit it off perfectly; they would still hang out from time to time. Tabby said he was a little too crazy for her. Tabby was my favorite cousin. She was seven years older than I was and she taught me a lot when I was younger. She was smart and loved money as much as I did. She always had a cat holding her down ever since back in Omaha. She always got what she wanted, and wasn't sleeping with half of the men that gave it to her.

We were already on a new crew of cats from L.A. We would go to L.A. with them shop, smoke, eat and just kick it hard. They were cool, and we could get anything we wanted from them. They loved us because we were go getters. I would hook them up with cats that needed work. Tabby, Tracy and I lived together, and we never got into fights with each other. We were true to one another and we did everything together but share men. It seemed like whenever we started liking someone everybody wanted them. They were always nice looking and had money. Tabby and I liked fat boys with fat pockets so if they were clean and smelled good, they were in. Charlie was my sister but also my best friend, she had a man, and he was strict, smart, had money, but jealous of everyone she hung around, even of me. He told her that we were whores and that she couldn't hang out with us. We weren't whores we just liked money; we weren't sleeping with men for money. We were getting our own. She still came around, after all, we were blood sisters, and no man was going to come between us. Her man was school friends with Reggie and Big Scooter. They always had work, weed, and money. Reggie was the one who put me in the game when I was seventeen; he was tight with the money though. If you asked Reggie for something, he would make you work for it. He had money but was stingy as hell. You would have never thought they were drug dealers because they looked like schoolboys, and stayed under the radar, the hell with flashing, they flossed on important things like buying property, what I should have been doing, I was too busy running around the United States. Big Scooter would come over and blow about a half ounce a day and drink on a case of Corona. He was my boy he and his crew gave me the name Queen; they loved me, shit I would have loved me too. I would help them get off so much chronic that they would always take care of me. Anthony was still on his hustle, so I was good. Anthony still had everyone in town on pins and needles when he was around. One night we were at

Club 95 kicking it hard. Anthony and his boys had brought out the Remy Martin, and then we swapped over to that nasty cheap Hennessey, that had all of us drunk. He saw a guy that we all knew from his neighborhood, he walked up to the guy and knocked him clean out with the glass that he was drinking from! The cats that were supposed to be so hard in town had just witnessed their boy get put to sleep, and not make one move as he laid on the pool table, they claimed to be thorough but knew who to mess with and who not to. I asked him later once we were home, why he hit that man like that, and embarrass him in front of everyone, I always thought dude was a gangster, but not then, he slept for a while. Anthony explained that when he was a kid the cat that he hit had dropped him in front of some other dudes and took his gold nugget ring. That's when I knew Anthony was a crazy motherfucker and that he didn't play. I asked him why he flipped out about something that happened so many years ago, especially about a played-out nugget ring, he said it was the Hennessey, and the devil got into him. Shit, the devil was in him all along.

Anthony was nuts but had a good heart; he was well mannered around his elders he was only bad when he got a hold of the wrong liquor, and maybe at the wrong times.

Besides that, he was cool; he stayed well dressed; he was dark chocolate, with the sexiest smile, plus he was bankrolled up fresh. All that turned me on about him, I looked past his craziness. I knew if someone messed with me they would literally disappear.

One day he was with a cat from the west that I introduced him to, Lucky. He had been doing his thing around town, I told Anthony that he was good people but don't believe everything that he said because he was real slick, and a fast talker. I had been skeptical of some of the Cali cats coming in town. The Cali boys would come around and give the cats in town low prices, and keep their money. I told him that he couldn't trust everyone. If you were in a game who could you trust?

Lucky was in the city getting it in, and he had bricks on deck, he told me to turn him on to some cats that would buy several. He said that he would kick me down some cash for the hookup. Since I only sold weed, I introduced him to Anthony. They got cool and started making deals. Anthony dealt with Lucky a few times, and everything went well. Lucky told Anthony if he went to L.A. with him that he could do even better numbers then what they were already doing. He gave him a price and told him to think about it. Anthony was so excited about the prices Lucky was talking about that he was ready to take the trip to the land, we called Cali. He asked my cousin Tabby and me to come; Lucky said it was cool because we're the ones that hooked them up. But my subconscious was telling me not to go; my cousin Tabby said she wasn't going either with all that money on the plane. I had already been stopped before at LAX. One time I had thirty thousand dollars on me to buy some weed, and when I arrived, two Hispanic undercover police officers escorted me away to the small jail at the airport they questioned me to see if had anyone to tell on, took my cash, and let me go. After I got out of there, I said that I would never go through the airport again with more than ten thousand dollars in my pocket. Nobody could get us to carry dope or money from state to state. If they got the product to us, we would move it. Anthony begged me to go West with him. He said he was only taking, eighty thousand dollars with him. He said tuts we're gonna come up and I'm going to take care of you, you can get a new car. As good as it sounds my gut was telling me different, he was doing well to me without taking that kind of risk. He had houses he owned cars, trucks, and everything. He was good but Lucky told him fifteen thousand dollars would get him a brick and that's all he could think about. He was now getting them for twenty- two five and that was a big difference. He was ready to do this deal, and do it big. I told Anthony, Lucky had fall off and had no money right now. Lucky's connect had gotten messed up, and money wasn't flowing. I warned Anthony that I didn't think that going to Cali was a good idea, he told me since I felt that way he wouldn't go. We decided to go out and went to Anthony's and my favorite restaurant,

Houston's. He forgot about the trip to Cali. I ordered my Hawaiian rib eye as usual and had two shots of Remy Martin VSOP. While we were at Houston's Anthony told me that he had a child on the way, he told me not to be upset because it was the chick that he was with before we had started messing around. I was with her; I had forgotten she even existed. I was a little threatened, but I brushed it off, I tried to justify it in my mind by saying that he wasn't my man even though I wasn't having sex with anybody else at the time. I told myself I didn't love him; I just liked him a lot. I didn't let my feelings get in the way with any man. I knew how the D-boys moved around, from past experiences, and that's the kind of men I attracted, so I went with the program.

The week had gone by fast. Anthony and I were supposed to hook up and go chill in the Ozarks. We were going to have a lovely romantic weekend in a cabin just the two of us. I couldn't wait. I called and called and didn't get an answer that wasn't like Jason, not to answer my calls, even if he didn't stop by he would call or answer the phone when I called him. I had a bad feeling and prayed that he was okay. He was always into something, so I always prayed for him. It was hard for a young man to survive in Kansas City, Killa City as we called it. They were always robbing and killing in our town. I knew Anthony could take care of himself but I still worried. I didn't like worrying, that was a sin, I had enough on my plate to be thinking that something terrible would happen to him. I just wanted to think positive but negative thoughts were going through my mind.

I had been calling Anthony since Wednesday, and he still had not answered my call, it was time for our trip to the Ozarks. I needed a drink, so Tabby and I drove to the liquor store, we grabbed a fifth of Remy Martin, Arbor Mist wine, and Philly blunt cigars. We said that we were going home to drink, and smoke. Vickie was at the house waiting on us. She had done Angels hair so that she could go with Jon-Jon's sister for the weekend. It was Friday night, and the clubs didn't really party on Fridays. To make the best out of the situation, we called Mac and his boys and had us an instant party. Mac came through with his clan. They had XO Remy Martin and a fat sack of Purp, Mac always did it big, if he wasn't sipping on XO he was on Cristal champagne. We had a super smoke session; we were straight Kansas City Chiefs and not the team. Mac would have us so high that we would be feeling paralyzed. I smoked so much I couldn't get any higher. Smoking that weed gave us the munchies, so I started cooking my famous fried chicken, and homemade fries. I don't know what field they were picking that bud from, but it was the best herb in the world. The Grape Street that's what we called it. We sat around listening to Tupac singing *All Eyes On Me* and the Luniz; *I Got Five On It*. We were smoking and chopping it up. It was us against the world. A few hours went by, when the phone rang, it was Jason number. He was on the phone talking to me like everything was cool, ignoring the fact that I had been calling him for days and he wasn't returning my calls, plus, he had stood me up. He said that he was out of town. I asked, out of town, and where, because we were supposed to be in the Ozarks this weekend. He told me that he was in Cali and that he had taken a chick with him to carry his money for him. I said so you went and did something that I told you not to do. I was pissed off! I told him that he could kiss my ass, I was about to hang up, but he stopped me. He told me that he should have listened to me because Lucky had already hit him up for his cash all I could do was shake my head. I asked him what happened. He said that Lucky and some broad had picked him and the chick that carried the money, up from the airport. They rode around grabbed some liquor and smoke, then went to check into a hotel room on Century. He said that once they pulled up to the hotel, he and the chick got out of the car to check in. Once they checked in and went back out to get their bags out of the trunk Lucky was gone. Anthony wasn't thinking at all, he had got comfortable with Lucky and got caught slipping.

Thank God, he had got robbed respectfully if that makes any sense, meaning there had been no gunplay involved. He said at least I only brought fifty thousand dollars because I was going to pay eighty thousand. I told him that he should be glad and thank God that he was alive and that the way his money was stolen was a blessing. It could have ended in gunplay because one way or another Lucky was going to get him I told him that he couldn't trust those Cali cats. I guess he thought I was playing when I told him that Lucky was short on cash. Lucky was okay now because he was fifty thousand dollars up without having to do anything but drive off and leave Anthony and that trick that he was with in the hotel parking lot. She wouldn't be getting any goodies this trip.

Chapter 9
Dirty Game

I started partying and kicking it again, as usual, me, Charlie, Tracy and Tabby were hitting the streets, all the cats were choosing one of us, by this time I was over the played-out cats in K.C.

We were all ready to get back to Vegas to the Mike Tyson vs. Holyfield fight, we were sure that we would find some new cats in Vegas when you're single why not play? I loved going to Vegas when there was a fight. Mike Tyson brought out all the baller, and broads from every state, me and my crew would for sure be in attendance. After going to Vegas with Anthony I said the only way that I would go back with a guy, was if they were my man, there were so many little brothers around that I thought that I was going to lose my mind, shit who takes sand to the beach. Anthony and I were still cool, even though he had some chick pregnant, and other women. I didn't care about what he had going on when he wasn't with me, and that wasn't often, but on this trip, I was single and ready to mingle.

My brother J. Bo came up from St. Louis for a car show before we left for Vegas. We were always eager when it came to kicking it with him and his crew. They had money, and everyone had new whips. We went to their hotel in Overland Park and kicked it. Some of his partners were arrogant, they acted like the world revolved around them, but we were boss chicks, and we could handle them. Out of respect for J. Bo I never slept with anyone in his crew, and year to date I still haven't. They liked hoes and strippers. I was a hustler getting my own money and balling harder than some of them. After the weekend was over and we had smoked up a few ounces of chronic bullshitting around, J. Bo went back to STL and I got back on my grind.

Jason had finally shown back up, by the house after all the commotion that had gone down with him getting robbed in L.A. We talked about what had happened; I didn't want to throw it in his face any more about me telling him not to deal with lucky. I told him how happy I was to see him alive I hugged and kissed him on the neck, causing an instant erection. We walked back to the house, went straight to the bedroom, immediately got naked and fucked like we hadn't seen one another in years, and then we made love. Everything was good, but he was still fifty thousand down making Jason turn into Anthony. I knew he was up to no good! He didn't like taking losses. By the end week, I was getting calls that he had taken some out of town cat for his cash. It was thirty to forty thousand dollars. I didn't have respect for men that robbed people; now my dude was doing it. The cats that he had robbed, homeboys were calling me, he said that they were in town to score and ended up getting jacked. I didn't know anything about it, and there wasn't' anything I could do. He told me that he was telling me because he knew I was Jason's chick so if anything jumped off, He said the dudes knew me, so he wanted to warn me.

I asked Anthony about the robbery; his reply was an evil, cruel grin. Then he became angry, saying what the fuck that nigga mean, he's warning you? Sounds like a threat to me. I'll kill all those niggas if they put you in anything. Jason was very protective of anyone he cared for. He always wore that grin when he had done something treacherous. Now he had gone to his dark side, looking enraged.

He said remember what you said to me on the phone when I called that night that Lucky got me? I asked what did I say? He replied the game is dirty. Those niggas got played, he said them niggas is hoes, and they know where I am at all day on 59th Street, I'm not hiding. They did know where he was, but they never tried to retaliate so I guess they were hoes or knew he wouldn't play with them. I hated to see or hear about people getting robbed, but it was the game. I prayed that it never happened to me again.

Anthony gave me money to go shopping, to shut me up about what he had done, we ate and smoked. He stayed at my house more than his own. Even though there were other women, they never got the time with him that I did. I tried talking to other guys, but Anthony wasn't going for it, he had several women that I was hearing about, but didn't want me with anyone. One day I invited this cat from Kansas over that I had been crushing on, we were chilling out and smoking. He was just a homeboy that came over from time to time to buy sacks. He hung around one of my play brothers Peanut, and they were the fly guys of Kansas and Missouri. I hadn't seen Jason in days; he had been spending time with his son that had just been born. I knew his baby momma was glad that she had dropped her load because this was the most she had seen him in months. I was enjoying Dudes company when Jason popped up at my house. He came in, checked out the seen, looking crazy as hell, as he walked in, we spoke. I didn't say anything else to him after we talked because he hadn't called in days, so basically, I played him off. He finally couldn't take it.

He called my name from the steps, telling me to come upstairs. I told Darren I would be back and followed him upstairs, Tracy, was in her room across from mine, when she saw Anthony she shook her head, and shut her door, knowing that he was there for trouble. I walked in the room he put his hands around my neck and started choking me, saying "Don't try to play me!" I was terrified because I knew how he was, hoping that he wouldn't go and say or do anything to Darren. I was dizzy and shocked that he was carrying on in this manner. He had choked the shit of me to the point I had lost my breath and almost lost consciousness. My friend was still sitting downstairs; I was scared for him. Anthony was crazy, and he knew exactly how to make niggas disappear. At this point, I told Tracy to tell my friend to leave. Her reply was "No, I'm not getting in it. That nigga is crazy baby." I was crying, embarrassed, and scared to go downstairs. My friend was still sitting there smoking and lounging, not knowing that this fool I was dealing with was a walking time bomb. He finally told me he had something to do and left. I was so happy but crazy Anthony was still around, mad dogging me, I wanted him to leave and go where he had been, but now he seen that I wasn't going to sit around like a fool and wait on him, he wasn't going anywhere. He told me he loved me and he was jealous, he then pulled me over to the bed saying let him make it up to you, I told him, that I didn't want to make up, which made him upset, he said that I must have been fucking and he wanted to see. He started grabbing at my pants I told him that I hadn't done anything with anyone, and to stop. I didn't want to have sex with him. We all know how that goes, he took my pants off, pulled my thong to the side, and stuck his dick inside of me, as hard as he could, he didn't care that I said no, I couldn't fight the feeling and gave in, he told me that's what I wanted, and fucked me like he had never done before. I guess he had a point to prove. I was right back a damn fool. Later that night, Tabby, Tracy, and myself were sitting around chatting and smoking as usual. Anthony and his boy Budda was still there. Thank God, my daughter, Angel was down the street, at Charlie's house. Mac had stopped by, with a few of his homies he came to smoke and drink that bottle of Cristal he was holding. We were always popping bottles with Mac. We were all sitting in the kitchen, discussing different things, and situations, and talking about our upcoming vacation to Vegas, we got into a heavy discussion about men and women being hoes. Everyone was going back and forth and talking over each other, and no one would let Jason say what he wanted. We were all talking loud over each other. When he couldn't get in what he wanted to say, he pulled out his nine-millimeter, shooting right through the ceiling. Everyone became silent and looked at that crazy fool. I was shocked and a little scared. He was crazy as hell. Tracy was in the bathroom talking to Budda. She said when she heard the shots; she thought that he had shot Mac. Budda grabbed her and wouldn't let her out the bathroom. Budda knew that Anthony was crazy, and he had to have his back. Tracy was terrified not knowing what was going on in the kitchen. Anthony jumped up after he saw us all looking. Tabby tried to run out the house, she knew he was crazy. He chased her and brought her back in. Anthony then told us he wasn't going to hurt anyone, he just really wanted to talk. He was a crazy motherfucker and I was crazy for loving him. We let him say his piece, and we were right back smoking as if he had never popped off. Mac wasn't scared, he was calm, and told Anthony to calm down. Mac was always telling him to slow it down, and was always trying to give him advice. He was at least ten years older than Jason.

After that incident, I said that I didn't need Jason around because he was too damn crazy. He didn't go anywhere because he was having issues at home. His baby momma called the police on more than one occasion. One thing I had never done and will never do was put the cops in my business, especially if I knew that I would be right back with someone. That was a no-no. I was moving my weed, so I couldn't have called if I wanted to. Anthony was nice after that. I heard that he was sneaking around smoking sherm. If he was smoking that shit that would explain his up and down mood swings, and I knew that I would have to leave him alone, period.

I started flying back to the west doing my business. Tabby would go with me most of the time. Me, Tabby, Tracy, and my sister Charlie did everything together. If a crew wanted to holler at one of us, most of the time we all ended up dating their friends. Trecie had moved back up north, so we hadn't been seeing her.

I knew I had to start breaking away from Jason; and traveling would get him out of my system. While we were out west, I ran back into Shona's uncle that I dated back in the day he was sexy, tall, dark, and slim, his name was Chico. He was digging me, he knew that I knew everyone in town, and had significant connections. He was moving work, with his boy Steve-Loc. Tabby and Steve-Loc ended up dating, that relationship turned out to be a jackpot. We started flying out west often to visit them. Chico liked kids and he hit it off with my daughter; he always bought her things. Trips to the mall always ended with her receiving something new. She was spoiled, but I still could have been a better parent, since Jon was in federal prison, my way of showing love was giving, gifts.

Chico knew that Jason was still a major factor in my life. Jason was my baby, he just had serious issues, plus I didn't need the baby momma drama. Months went by, and we were hanging out more and more with Chico and C-Lo, they got a spot in the city. We would go over and smoke with cats from the north and the south. I was gradually growing apart from Jason.

One day, we were sitting down at Big Skoot's spot, smoking and drinking Corona's. Skoot always kept a deep freezer of chronic and a case of Corona's. He had hooked up with my girl Mina. She was young and fast as hell. She had niggas, but it didn't matter if she cheated or not, Skoot loved her. I tried hooking Tracy up with Skoot, but they ended being good friends instead. He would let Mina have the keys to the house, and when my weed supply went out, Mina would get handfuls of chronic to smoke. We were chilling when I received a phone call that Anthony had gone to jail. I knew I hadn't heard from him in a couple of days, nothing unusual. It was the worst news ever; they said that he was at his house, cooking cocaine, and a fight started between him and his baby's moms. She phoned the police and told them that he had drugs in the house, and was burying them in the back yard. The police arrived and found kilos of cocaine. They brought him downtown to the police station. I was so hurt, questioning what I would do without him. A week had gone past, Jason was released, on bond, no matter what, I would hold him down. He was stressed because he couldn't move like he wanted to, he could only chill. He was going through his case and waiting on sentencing. He didn't want to accept the deal they were offering him, so he packed up and went on the run.

While Anthony was, running, I started hanging out with the girls to occupying my time. Chico left Kansas City and moved to Vegas. Every time there was a fight in Vegas we were there, my crew had expanded, and we were even deeper going to Vegas. We didn't miss a Mike Tyson fight. Vegas and L.A. was our spot, and we were living it up. When we were in Vegas men always tried to solicit us for sex. We were on the elevator in the MGM when a guy stepped to me and asked me did I want to make some money. I told him hell no; he told me that I had just missed my blessing. I laughed and kept it moving. Chicks came out to Vegas to sell pussy but we didn't have to because we were drug dealers and we didn't have to sell our body to get money, we came with our stacks. If I wanted to have friendly pussy, it would be on my time and the guy that I chose.

Jason had set up shop in Denver and moved his operation there. I had people there that I knew; it truly is a small world, One of Tabby's friends from Omaha lived there. She had met Jason at a bar, he told her that he was from Kansas City but gave her his alias name, she told him that her family lived there throwing all of our names out, but he never responded, that same night he met her, he fucked her, even if he told her, that I was his chick, he still could have got in her pants. I found out. I asked him about it; he admitted that he fucked her and didn't give her twenty bucks. She looked good fucking for free, especially with someone that would have laced her pockets well. I visited a couple of times and made sure that I hooked up with her, and also let her know that she should have made his ass pay because he most definitely paid me for what he had done with her.

Anthony became tired of making moves in Denver. He gave me ten thousand dollars to find us a spot in Dallas. He said once I found the spot that he would send more cash and be on his way. That's just what I did, I wanted to move out of the Kansas City anyway, and this was the perfect opportunity, even though he was running from the feds.

I was going to get Angel and be out but I needed to secure my spot before I'd bring my baby down. My childhood friend Abby drove me down to North Dallas. We checked into a hotel, and the next morning we headed out to find an apartment. I found an apartment that day, of course, money talks, so we were set. I dropped a few months of rent down on the spot and was ready to move in and be with Jason.

Abby brought Angel down to me a week later. We had a two-bedroom apartment, with a loft, and a sunroom. It was beautiful. While I was there, I met a chick from Beaumont, Texas named Anna. She was adorable and had a twin sister. She worked at Wendy's; she didn't have much but was still grateful for what she did have. She showed me around we ended up being good friends. After getting unpacked, I gave her a lot of clothes that I didn't wear anymore. I've never really had to wear hand me downs, so I didn't know that it brought so much joy for someone to give you something. When my mom brought me hand me downs from the garage sales, I cried, because I didn't want to wear some strangers clothing. She was so happy and was looking good in those clothes. Reggie's uncle had a condo in Texas; he also looked out for us. I was a blessed woman especially with how I was living on the edge for the man I loved.

Jason was still living in Denver, trying to make his way to Angel and me. Two months had passed, and he was still not there, he sent more money for the rent, the bills were all paid up. I was fine, and so was Angel. She was in school and doing very well. From time to time, Angel would complain about wanting to go back home, because she missed everyone. I would tell her to wait for Anthony, when he arrived, we would have much more fun. Momma's word was bond. I would call home to talk with my son, Lil' B, and they would always have an excuse. Either he was out of town or at a game somewhere. They were also telling him, I was a drug dealer, a whore, a thief, whatever they could to turn him against me. I missed my son and wanted to make things right with him. When I would buy, his shoes or clothes, his step-mother would tell me to buy him cheaper things because her boys didn't have the same stuff, I wanted him to have the best like we had, more than anything I wanted him to know me, and to know that I loved him.

My new-found friend Anna had told me about, these cats, that she had met some months back, and how they always had bomb weed, they lived in the same complex as we did, one day they invited us over to drink and smoke with them. Anna's twin sister watched Angel for me as she would often do, and off we went to the "weed man's" apartment. Once we went into the apartment, I walked into what seemed to be a marijuana lab. There were FedEx boxes of weed everywhere, triple beams, digital scales, at least twenty packs of zip lock bags, and fifths of liquor. I was astonished; she wasn't playing when she said they had it going on. It wasn't Cush, but it wasn't dirt either, it had a nice minty taste. I was thinking, as country as she was, she was up on something. As always, I was looking fly; I had on a sexy Adrienne Vittadini jersey dress and a pair of sexy sandals, I topped it off with my thousand-dollar tennis bracelet, which glistened every time I moved. I noticed they were checking me out. One kept telling me how much he liked my gold fronts, and how good I was smelling good, and I kept a nice fragrance on always, I was a perfume diva. I had on Versace Blonde. The more told me how sexy I was, the more weed I rolled, he gave, Anna an ounce and told her to split it with me, he told us to let our friends check it out, and they could get at him on whatever they wanted. I had already told him that I didn't know anyone in Dallas I guess that was his way of being kind or trying to get in my pants. We were blowing just like I did in K.C., it made me think of home. As we drank and smoked they bagged up pounds of weed. My mind was racing; I couldn't believe how much weed these cats had. Someone knocked on the door, that they knew, I overheard them talking, he wanted a pound or two. The first cat went to the door to take the order, for whatever reason, he started getting slick, and they ended up having some confrontation. I thought dude was arrogant, showing off for us, talking crazy to the guy as he walked outside of the house, one thing led to another and shots started ringing out from outside. All I could think about was my children. Now it felt like home. Niggas was shooting; I was scared and confused, my heart felt like it was going to pop out of my chest. I was wondering, how the hell was I going to get out of this? I ran to the back of the apartment, looked down, and jumped right over the second story balcony like a track star doing hurdles. Somewhere in the process, I lost my thousand-dollar bracelet. I can remember praying to God and jumping. He always saw me through; this would be one of those days I needed him most. I ran all the way to Anna's apartment, without stopping or looking back, grabbed Angel, and hugged her tight. Anna had come through the door looking at me puzzled asking "How did you get out of there?" I replied God. Girl, I jumped off the balcony" was my simple reply. After it was over, I laughed, but I was scared as hell when it happened. The Lord has brought me through on many different occasions, and this was just another example of that. My faith in God brought me out of there.

"And he said to her, Daughter, your faith has made you whole. Go in peace, and be healed of your affliction" (Mark 5:34).

I laid around waiting for Jason to call that evening, he had a specific phone that he used since he was wanted by the U.S. Marshalls, when he called I told him what had happened and that he needed to hurry up and get here, I didn't want to be alone anymore, the bills were paid and everything was good, but I moved there for him and he wasn't there with me, had he been there I never would have been in that apartment, but then again with him there, things could have been worse. He told me that he had to wait on a few more people In Arizona, and Denver to cash him out and he would be on his way. He promised no longer than two more weeks of me waiting, we'd finally be together, I was eager to see him, plus I hadn't had sex in three months. The next couple of weeks, I would clean the house, awaiting the arrival of my man. Angel and I would go out to eat almost every night or over to Reggie's cousin's house to hang out. I was patiently waiting to be reunited with my man. A week had passed; I finally had received a call from Jason. He said everything was looking good and he would be on his way in a few more days. He wired me a thousand dollars. Too bad I wasn't in

Kansas City; I went straight to Victoria Secret's to find something sexy to wear for him. In the back of my mind, I knew that it would be coming right off. I also purchased candles at the Yankee Candle Company and finished off with a bottle of Chanel perfume. I was ready to sex Jason up; I had a babysitter for Angel. I would show him just how much I missed him; it was on. The next week came, and I wanted it to go by quickly, but it seemed to drag. At the Same time, I was on a job hunt with Anna, I was no longer selling drugs and didn't want to only depend on Jason I was spending money but didn't have an income. The money Anthony gave me was getting short, and I didn't want to go in my stash. I liked Texas, but I missed my family. I would call Tabby and Charlie; we would talk for hours. They missed me as much as I missed them. After all, we were inseparable.

Tracy had been arrested and sent to the penitentiary for a violation, I missed her as well, that was my ride or die, and I was lonely because we were all apart, at least if I was in town, I could visit her in Kansas and take her all the contraband that she needed. She didn't need or want for anything because we made sure she had everything. Guards were worse than the inmates. They would bring things into the jails, and in some cases, even getting the female inmates pregnant. Jail is just like the streets. Visits to see Tracy showed all the corruption front and center. She was a boss in prison and told us the "rights" and "wrongs, the "do's" and "don'ts" of the system, I never wanted to end up there.

It was the end of the week, and I was glad it was finally over; my man was on his way. I thought about it; I hadn't heard from him, I figured I'd hear from him because it was the weekend, we talked every weekend, it was a sure thing. Saturday came, then Sunday, then Monday, and I still hadn't heard anything from Jason. I was upset; it had been three months since I'd seen him, the bills were always paid up. So, I stuck it out. Dallas was my new city. I knew he would show up anyway. By the end of the week, I received a call, the one no one wants to get. The feds had tracked him down and snatched him up, by tracing a phone call. I was devastated. I cried for the rest of the week. I didn't care that the rent was paid up for another two months; I wanted to go home and be closer to my family and my king. After a call to my friend Abbey, without hesitation, she drove back to Texas to get Angel and me. We packed up and made our journey back home.

Chapter 10
New Beginnings

I was back in Kansas City, and Jason was in jail. As hurt as I was, I always knew this day would come. I would visit him, and we always stayed in contact on the phone. He even proposed. I was so down for him; I called the court to see how to start the process. One day, my sister Charlie asked me one real question, "Why would you want to marry someone in jail, not only jail, but he's going to prison for lord knows how long?" She had me thinking real hard at that point. I was young, and Jason was facing fifteen to twenty-five years. I felt that he loved me, but at the same time he also loved his son's mother, even though she was the one that got him into this situation, and there wasn't any telling who else he was selling dreams too.

While Jason was awaiting sentencing, I got back to cooking and making money. I promised myself that I was finished hustling, prison had everyone's name on it. That didn't last long before I knew it I was back to getting weed from Mac. As always Mac came through for me. He brought me a pound of the prettiest Cush that I had ever seen. I broke the buds down and started back selling weed. After about three weeks all my customers were back, and I was back on track. A month passed, and I had enough money to get a couple of pounds on my own. Pounds went for forty-five hundred to six thousand dollars in 1996, and I would make at least ninety-five hundred off each pound, things were going good, and I was back on my grind.

Anthony was still my heart, and I was making that trip to Leavenworth, but marriage was out of my head by now. I loved him but realized that I wasn't in love. I just couldn't get married. I wanted a beautiful church wedding and not a jail wedding. Plus, I knew I wasn't his one and only girl. Months flew by, and I was trying to stay focused on myself, Angel and making money. Little B's dad started coming around, so things were getting back on track. Anthony was about to be sentenced, and I found out that he was about to marry his son's mother, it didn't bother me it was a relief; better her than me I thought. I was happy for him and had no reason to be mad; he received fifteen years federal time.

Through it all, we wrote each other and remained friends. Jason had done a lot for me and the least I could do was return the favor and write him.

Chapter 11
On to the Next One

I started back hanging out and traveling. I would go to St. Louis to see Skooter. He was always there for me, we still never had sex, but I called him my man every time I went to see him. I would always leave with a few thousand or better. He was sexy and slim; he reminded me of Chico my west coast boo. They were Snoop Dog looking cats with hella swag. St. Louis wasn't far, from K.C., but it was far enough to get away and have peace of mind.

Freaknik in Atlanta was coming up in April, the girls and I had been every year since we heard about it 1994, 1995 now it was 1996.

We would make that twelve-hour drive to the ATL. We'd get to Atlanta fast; at least it seemed like it. I would drive or Tracy. We would sing songs and smoke chronic all the way there speeding and hoping we didn't get pulled over. Gerald Levert would be playing most of the time, or, E-40, Mac Dre or Rich the Factor, Rich was a cat from the home town that I would hang out with on occasion, we smoked plenty of chronic together. He had good gangster riding music, so that's what we had in the CD player all the way down to the A.

We finally arrived on Friday morning. We checked into the Hyatt Regency in Downtown Atlanta. We always stayed there because we could walk everywhere and downtown was always popping during Freaknik. We were so hyped that no one wanted to sleep. We were ready to do our thing, we had all new clothes, and we were ready to get fly and meet new cats. I was always meeting new people even chicks. Meeting females was my way of getting to know people in other states where I might set up shop and expand my business. I had brought with me a half pound of chronic; I was ready to work and play. Atlanta didn't have chronic in the city, they were still burning dirty brown weed, so I knew I could double my money by selling my weed for more. Back in Kansas City, a half ounce went for three hundred, fifty dollars; I was selling a half ounce in the ATL for five hundred dollars. The extra cash would pay for my trip and shopping. All I had to do was fire up, and cats would come running following that bomb chronic. The word would get out, and I would be able to move my product in no time. I'd make even more money in the club. I would break the ounces down and sell sacks. When we lit up in the club, we would have everybody coming to holler at us. Like Toucan Sam says; just follow your nose. We kicked it so hard in Club 112 that we never would realize, the time. It was seven in the morning when we left out this time. We always made sure that we went there we had the time of our life every time we went, we never paid to get in. Cats would pay our way or somehow, I'd boss up and got us all in. After all, I was a Lady Boss, and it didn't go unnoticed. We got back to the hotel and slept for about four hours and we were back at it again. We had only been there one day, and I was almost out of weed. I still had my fat sack, but we smoked like hell in the club the night before.

It was a lovely Saturday, sunny skies, we all were loving it because it was still cold back in K.C. we were good in our spring wear that we couldn't wear at home. We headed out to Lenox Mall and did some shopping. Even though we had all new gear, ATL had way more flier, and exotic things to choose from, than we had at home, we wanted things that we could take back home, and the city wouldn't be ready for it. Lenox was off the chain; people were everywhere. It was so packed that they announced that they would shut down early. Tracy hit up a few stores and boosted some top-notch items. Wherever we went she hit up the stores for something fly, and expensive; she would always hook us up as well. We all had a bankroll, but if you could get it for free, that was even better. I came up with a few numbers in the mall no one that caught my eye, but that's what Freaknik was all about, fucking for some, getting numbers and networking for others. We headed over to Peachtree Street to hang out; it was bananas.

Chicks were walking around naked; they were in cars giving head. Dudes were walking around with their dicks out. It was wild, and we loved it, but we were boss chicks, we would have never participated in that kind of activity. Later that evening we got dressed in our new gear, and we went back to Club 112. I met a fine light skinned cat named Martez. I have never liked red men, but he was fine as hell, smelled good and had a lot swagger he was about six feet, three inches tall, two hundred pounds and had some of the sexiest lips that I had ever seen. They reminded me of LL. Cool J when he licked his lips. I wanted to grab his face and kiss him right there, and I didn't even like kissing. I was standing in the corner drinking on a glass of Cristal, smoking my blunt. I felt someone watching me when I turned around it was Sexy Red with those luscious lips. He had been checking me out, just like I was checking him out. Tabby said go holler at him, we was going to the restroom. I was a boss chick so if he wanted me he would have to make the first move. I and Tabby never danced we just stood back and peeped the scene. My sister Charlie, on the other hand, would dance all night. Men loved to see Charlie dance she had a big ass and she could shake it. The club was about to close, and we were leaving out when the sexy cat with the luscious lips finally approached me. We started talking, he told me that his name was Martez then he asked me what was mine. I told him my name was Queen, he laughed saying, Queen huh? I said yes, Queen "he said I want to know your government name. I never told people my real name; I was digging him, so I told him, "my name is Demetria," he said Demetria?" I responded, yes" he said I like that, I said I like you. He laughed saying that I was clever; whatever that meant, if he only knew. We talked for a minute he told me that he was from East, St. Louis; I told him that I was from Kansas City, that was even better we wouldn't have far to see one another. He said, so it's like that in K.C? I responded it sure is; he laughed and licked his luscious lips once again, making me moist. I thought I was going to melt; shit had he asked he could have gotten the goods that night. I was feeling him. We exchanged numbers and went our separate ways. The parking lot was so crunk that I still had time to check out the scene and get more numbers, but after meeting Martez, I didn't want to meet anyone else. My gut said leave, but my mind wouldn't let me it was playing tricks on me. The cats were still choosing up, and being how I was, I didn't turn down anything but my collar so therefore, I was on to the next one.

After leaving the club, we met up with some guys and went to the Waffle House and ate breakfast. There was a Waffle House on every corner in the Atlanta, and it was just about the only place to eat that early in the morning. The cats we ate breakfast with were from Tennessee they were cool for one of the girls, but I had Martez on the brain, they were good for a free meal and a little conversation. We ate, they paid for our food, and they left. We sat there in the Waffle House and chilled for a minute, talking about relationships. I told them how I missed Skooter, even though we hadn't slept together. I was telling them how he told me that he remembered the day that he met me and that I wasn't an ordinary chick. He said that I was a rare breed and he was glad that we met. He should have been glad that he met me. He made a lot of money dealing with me. Skooter was the only cat that I knew that would come to town with fifty thousand dollars, and I would never have to count it. He didn't even look like he had money. He looked like a college boy his clothes were regular, not like the arrogant fly cats that I usually hollered at. As the old saying goes, never judge a book by its cover. That look got him by with his drug runs all the time. That's how he always made it back and forth up and down the road. Skooter never sent mules to get what he needed; he always came alone. He never talked on the phone, and now I see why. Whatever moves he made he would tell me when we were face to face. He moved swiftly and in total silence. We never had any issues. The deal went well every time, and I would have five thousand extra dollars every time he left. I had money and chronic all the time.

I, Tabby, and her sister Vickie could smoke are asses off. Tracy smoked but not like we did. Charlie never smoked or drank, but she wasn't going to miss out on making that money or having a good time. Charlie broke up with her boyfriend, and we were back hanging tough. We looked a lot alike, so guys didn't care witch one of us they had they just wanted a piece of us, just to say they had us. Men would even lie and say they screwed us. Niggas are ridiculous and be telling lies on their dick.

We finally went back to the hotel so we could get some rest and get ready to take the journey back to K.C. We were tired, after all, we had only slept five hours out of three days, plus we smoked chronic, drank Remy Martin, and popped bottles, the whole time we were in the A, but we still had to go hard that Sunday night. We ended our weekend in a club called Otto's in Buck's head. There were ballers everywhere, and ballplayers. It was ridiculously crunk! I had myself a ball; I and the girls were doing our thing. I was smoking like a chief, but I had to slow down because I needed to have some weed left to drive home. I could drive for hours if I had a good smoke and some Gerald Levert playing. We took it in early around four am. That was early to us because we were getting in every morning at eight am, but we were leaving that Monday morning, so we needed to get a little sleep. The next morning, I gave Martez a call before we got on the road, come to find out he was in the hotel next door, he met me outside. We smooched on each other, had a nice chat, then he asked me to come to St. Louis to visit him the following week. He told me not to worry about anything because he would take care of everything. I would do just that. I was headed that way anyway because I had to see my brother J. Bo, so now I could kill two birds with one stone. St. Louis was three hours from my city, and I didn't mind driving.

The week went by fast. I wanted to spend time with Angel because I was always on the go. I took her to dinner a few times and took her shopping. I helped her with her homework and spent quality time with her. I was feeling guilty for leaving her all the time, but when you're in the life and have no guidance that's how it goes. Friday came, and I was STL. Bound but I didn't drive this time I flew. Martez picked me up from the airport. We hung out and had drinks and dinner. After dinner, we went to a lounge and got drunk. After that, he needed to take care of some things so I met up with my boy J. Bo so I could hang out with him.

I was happy to see J. Bo. We rode around talking and smoking. We rolled blunt after blunt; I was so high! I had reached my limit, but Bezzy was still passing blunts, and I was still hitting them. After I was finished kicking it and talking business with Bro., I called Martez to pick me up. J. Bo knew Martez because Bezzy was screwing one of Martez chicks. No one was tripping because that's just how it was. When ballers came out, the women knew who to choose, and Martez and J. Bo were in that circle of being chosen.

Martez picked me up; we got a room and went at it as soon as we closed the door. His sex was good; I was not disappointed at all. We screwed like we were together for years. I hadn't had a sex life since Jason had left, but Martez was great in the bed, and I was breaking him off and would be coming back for more. After what seemed to be four rounds of great lovemaking, we laid around talking. He admitted to me that he was a drug dealer, which was no surprise to me, he asked me did I know people that dealt drugs, I told him I did and I might be able to get him better numbers than he was currently getting. Martez was younger than me, which most of the men that I dealt with were, which made me feel I knew more than them, and I could put them up on the game. I could tell he was a dealer in Atlanta when I met him. He had the most fly clothes on, a nice chain, and a bracelet with an icy Rolex watch. It seemed like the only men that were attracted to me were drug dealers, and it seemed they were the only ones' I was attracted to also. I told Martez that I knew some big-timers that could hook him up with a lower price than what he said he was currently paying. That was music to his ears because he started coming into town getting what he needed. Unlike Scooter I always had to count his cash, it wasn't that much off, but it was never right. Now I was hooking them both up, and that was putting an extra eight thousand every two weeks in my pocket. What I said was I was out of that game, and I never sold cocaine, but I guess I did because I was the middleman in the deals, and could have gotten a lot of time doing it. I guess I'll say, indirectly I did. I had it going on, I was feeling good, and I felt like I was the shit. Martez never really had an issue but one time he said the work wasn't right, but he couldn't bring it back, after all, it wasn't mine I was just the middleman. That's how the game went, and I had some good connections so most of the time the product was good and I only dealt with people that I trusted, this time my people got him. I would hook Skooter and Martez up with who they needed to get their supply, but I was the Weed Lady, and that was my hustle. I still was catering and delivering dinners. I never got in trouble with the law thank God. I was just enjoying life; maybe it was time for me to stop doing what I was doing, get my kids and be a mom.

Months had gone by, and winter came fast. When the snow hit the ground, it was ground time. We still had to watch our backs, and we had to always worry about someone trying to jack us. People would always tell me this cat, and that cat was trying to rob me. There was no doubt in my mind that they would have, I knew that was part of the game, and I was always prepared I was never slipping even though I was doing wrong, God had my back.

Chapter 12
Caught Slipping

December came, and that was the time that the jackers were on the move. One day I got a call from Charlie's baby daddy, he told me that his boy wanted to cop some work from me. He wanted nine ounces, of hard, and a four and a half and he would pay whatever. It was Christmas time, and I needed extra cash, so I told him, and his boy could meet me on 81st St. and Troost at the grocery store. He said ok that would be cool. I told him five o'clock. I pulled up with Tabby at exactly five o'clock and waited about five minutes. That's when this OG cat walked up; I knew him. His son used to try and holler at me, so I was comfortable with the transaction. I got out the car to say hello because I knew him. I also knew that he had been shooting heroin, I didn't deal with junkies no matter how much money they had but since Charlie's baby daddy Mike, had hooked up the deal, I felt that it was all good.

I got out the car and was walking up to him to speak when he put a big silver Desert Eagle right on my face, between my eyes, and said give me the work! I don't want to shoot you. I knew he would if I didn't cooperate. I was like oh shit. I was scared as hell because I didn't want to go out like that behind a few ounces of dope, so I started praying and handed him the bag. He ran off, and nine thousand dollars was gone. I ran back to the car and told Tabby that TI's daddy had just robbed me. I was alive though; cats in my city would rob and kill you quick, so as long as I still had my life the money could be made back in one day, but my life couldn't be replaced! I immediately called Mike and asked him why did he set me up? He acted like he didn't know what I was talking about, but I knew he was lying because he knew that I knew TI's daddy and that I would never have dealt with him. I was outdone and felt betrayed by Mike. I thought he had love for me, but now I knew he had something to do with me getting robbed.

After the robbery, I said I was finished with drugs, but I was right back at it, such a fool, dancing with the devil. Christmas came, it was still good, we bought the kids everything, even though Lil' D was with his dad and they filled his head with all that scandalous shit about me, I still made sure that he had everything that he wanted. Angel had so much, everybody loved her, so she got gifts from everybody, and she had enough clothes to last for six months without wearing the same outfit twice. We had a great Christmas. New Year's came, and we popped bottles with King and Mac. Cristal and chronic for all; it was 1997. I was already planning my year out; it was going to be a good year. I already had a trip planned for Cancun Mexico on the calendar plus every year we were going to Atlanta for Freaknik. I was ready for both Freaknik in April and Cancun in May. It was going down in 1997.

I had also set up shop in the city I was born in Omaha Nebraska. I could go up there make a quick five to ten thousand dollars for a weekend and then go back to K.C. That would be my spending money for my trips. I needed new gear for all my trips, and it wasn't cheap. I was ordering Versace swims suits and bags to take on my trip. It was going to be P. Diddy's All-Star weekend in Cancun, so I was planning early. My father still lived in Omaha along with my three stepsisters. They were in foster care because their mom had got on drugs and couldn't keep them, I felt that she was one of the reasons that I couldn't stand dirty, trifling hoes, as I look back I realized she was a crackhead, she would leave for days when we were young, and come back hungry as hell eating anything that she could find the house. She had no respect for my father or her children. Charlie and I tried several times to get our sisters, and bring them home with us but they were in the system, and we couldn't get them. We talked to them and assured them we loved them. We sent bags of clothes to them because all our friends were boosters. I would pray at night for God to look out and take care of them. When I returned to K.C. Mac was still hanging with his homeboys that I didn't care for. I had a bad feeling about them, and soon I would know why. Mac had fallen out with his wife she left him and moved back to Oklahoma where she was from. Mac was depressed and not the same. He was still sleeping around, plus he was sleeping with my friend Marsha and a couple of other chicks that I knew, but he wanted his wife back. He would come over and smoke and stare into space. He was depressed. He had a lot more going on than just his wife leaving him. He had lost a lot of money messing with this town. Mac had his crew that he came into town with and they would always be with him, they knew he wasn't feeling the town anymore. They told him that maybe it was time to go to another state and set up shop. He had made K.C. his home, and he wasn't leaving.

Tabby messed with one of his boys named Duke, and the other two was Buck and Tuck not related, but names were similar, or at least that's the names they gave us. He also had moved his sister and cousin into town. They were not going back to Bakersfield, California. Mac opened a burger shop right next to the beauty shop that I went to on 18th and Brooklyn. The food was real, good. I would go there and sit for hours and chill at the burger spot. The spot took his mind off wifey. Burger World was doing great, and the beauty shop I went to was right next door. My stylist was gay and wild as hell; his name was Russie. It was like his mom gave him his name knowing that he would be a girl. He would go screw men while he left us in the shop for hours. He was the best in the city doing hair, in my eyes I wouldn't let anyone else do my hair but Russie, or Pete who worked in the shop also. Pete died of AIDS; I was so sad about it. There were a lot of Russie's friends that were dying of AIDS, but Russie's fast, nasty ass made it through. He was just as much a hoe as most of his clients. He had the most fly clientele in the hair game if you ask me. We didn't play any games from the working ones to the hustlers. I knew me and my girls were fly but he had sets of fly girls coming in and out of his shop, I give credit where credit is due.

My homeboys that hated punks were even cool with Russie because of me; I was glad that they weren't homophobic. He was the only punk that they would smoke with. I would go to Russie's shop and post up and sell weed. His shop was on the North side of town, and everybody smoked and wanted that exotic that I had. Chicks hated that I could walk in the beauty shop and get my hair done just like that. They would be there for hours, and I would take their turn but I was a boss, and that's what bosses do. I always took care of Russie. I loved gay men they were fun to be around, and he was fly, and his hair was whipped all the time. I would go from the beauty shop to Burger World selling weed. 18th and Brooklyn was a money-making spot; there was a barbershop and the food joint, Wings and Things there also. Mac and his boys use to always laugh at Russie saying that he was indeed a bitch and a damn fool at that. Russie would sleep with some of the girl's men whose hair he did. Their men were on the down low, and it was always the ones that no one would ever believe! The girls would find out and want to fight Russie. I never understood why they wanted to fight Russie because if my man were screwing a punk, I would dump his ass and keep it moving; I probably would have his ass smoked for screwing me then sticking his dick in a man's ass, or even letting one suck on him. We would laugh at the stories that Russie would tell us about how he screwed his customer's man right under their nose. He would say, well ole boy isn't gay, because he would only let me suck his dick, to any man that feels he's not gay because a man is giving him head, I have news for you, you're certifiably a punk!!! I talked to a couple of the women but never had enough courage to tell them that their man was a faggot. We would be high as hell cracking up. Russie was a mess, and I loved his mess, after all, I was a mess too, Jon-Jon had turned me into an "I don't give a fuck about a nigga kind of chick." I had no love for these cats I treated them just like they treated women like they weren't shit I gave them hell like they did weak minded females. A few guys would tell me; I act like a nigga. I would tell them, oh well you're not going to run over me so I'll take your cash, maybe have sex with them and be gone just like that; I was just like them.

I was missing Martez; he was kind of mad about his last trip. I wanted sex, and he was the only one that I was sexing at the time. I didn't like messing with cats in town at all. I would have given Richie rich some, but we were just friends, so I was horney as hell! There was Skooter, who I cared a lot for and thought about him like a boyfriend, but we were getting so much money together to where I didn't want to mix business with pleasure, so I never overstepped my boundaries, nor did he, we kept getting money.

Mac had been out of town, and I needed him back. He had been gone for two weeks I was buying weed from other people, and I didn't like spending money with other people. I was the Weed Lady, even though people gave me sacks and smoked with me I still was spending, because that's how much weed I smoked, but as they say don't get high off your supply, I was, and I was smoking up my profit, not saving for a rainy day. Seven grams was two hundred dollars or more, and I could smoke about a half ounce to an ounce a day, you add that up. That's a lot of money. My girls and I were true pot smokers, and we didn't smoke regular weed, chronic only. Martez finally called and asked me to come down to St. Louis to visit him. I was ecstatic. I wanted to see him. I hadn't had sex in over a month and needed to feel his touch. My conscious kicked in, I was a little fearful because he had got hit up by my people the last time that he got his drugs, they had given him some bad product, and he was very upset about it. But deep down in my heart I knew that he knew that I had nothing to do with it and that I would never do anything to him like that because my heart was genuine. I didn't condone anyone being scammed, but that's just how the game went, sometimes you win, sometimes you lose. I was true to the game. I also knew that St. Louis cats didn't play and would kill you for doing them wrong! I have never been the one for bad karma. Martez called back again saying that he wanted to see me, so I headed to the STL. When I arrived, he welcomed me with open arms after all, he still needed me because I had the connection for the prices he wanted. He had his own connect, but when they were out, he needed the Queen. We talked, and I apologized for what had happened and assured him that I would never have let anything like that happen if I had known. I let Martez know that my other people were good and they would never do anything to get me twisted up or hurt. Now everything was fine, and we were back good. We finally got to the sex that I had been craving for the last month. We never had four-play, but he got some super head this night, then we fucked the hell outta one another, now I had my glow back and my boo. I got up the next morning ready to head back to K.C. Martez said that he would be coming through by the end of the week. I knew I had to get back and get everything lined up. I kissed his luscious LL Cool J lips, which made us get in another round that was even better than the night before, then I headed back home.

I got home and talked to my connect. Martez had already told me that he would be bringing forty thousand dollars, that way we wouldn't have to talk on the phone and I could have everything ready and on point. Mac would arrive back in town right after I did; it was perfect timing. He would arrive Tuesday morning; I couldn't wait for Monday to get here, I sat around with Tabby and Vickie, they were close to Charlie and me. We drank on some Remy Martin and smoked a few blunts. I told them how my trip to STL went and that Martez would be coming through this weekend. Charlie had got back with her boyfriend, so she was missing in action. The good part was that she lived down the street, so we were always close to each other.

Tracy had met a new guy and had been dating him for a minute; she was telling me about her weekend with him and how well they connected. He was a baller in the city and was also married, but it didn't stop her from kicking it with her boo at all. Me and the crew loved each other, and we would tell each other about all our problems. We were true to each other, and were all doing our thing.

My cousin Vickie was a good girl that smoked as much weed as Tabby and me and could drink anybody under the table. She didn't sell drugs she was more laid back if she had weed and drink until she was satisfied. Me, Tabby and Tracy were ready for whatever. We loved money, made our own, and made sure we had a nigga to give us more. I also had a play daughter name Yoyo. I loved my little dark chocolate child; she helped me a lot with Angel, we all gave her anything she wanted. She dressed Angel, took her places; she was the definition of a true big sister. She had wrecked a few of my cars but I didn't even care because I would get them fixed, that's the life I was living. I traveled so much, and she was a true blessing for Angel and me, along with all the other people that looked out for Angel.

Jon-Jon was still in jail, but he always made sure that one of his boys looked out for Angel. Even though he wasn't around, he was still making it happen for his child, like a real man is supposed to do. I had a down click, and we were one hundred percent true to each other.

The next day Mac came back in town. I was happy to see my bro because he had been gone for a while, we talked, he told me that he had stopped in Oklahoma to see his wife and they were going to try and work their marriage out. I was so relieved to hear that they had worked things out after all, someone deserved to be happy. I was content, I didn't have a man of my own, but I had money, so I didn't care, at least I acted like I didn't, and I had a lot of cats trying to choose up, that I knew was no good for me, so I stayed free. That was my problem; I wanted men that I had to go through drama with instead of the good man that wanted to settle down with me and make me their woman, twerps I called them. I was always looking for a challenge. I was a player, playing the game, the only way I knew how. I told them all exactly what they wanted to hear; I had my daughter and my crew and my family, that's all that mattered. I also had my son Little B. regardless of what his father and stepmother were brainwashing him with, telling him about me, he still loved me, but from a distance. His dad took good care of him, and I didn't have to worry about anything, I don't know what his stepmom and his dad were telling him about me, but they had him scared straight! He didn't want to stay the night when he would come over. Even though I was out there doing my thing I had a lovely drama free home that was always clean and full of food, we lived and ate very well, I just so happen to sell drugs, and had I known better, I would have understood that his dad was only trying to protect him.

Mac told me that he would be coming back that evening with my weed. I was over excited because I had been out and I was spending money on sacks of weed, something that I hated to do. He owed me a few pounds because I had let him hold fifteen thousand of my cash because he had told me he would bring me something nice back. I spent money so fast to where I would always let him hold money for me. I was ready to work, plus the whole city was waiting on me. I kept that grade A chronic, and that's what they wanted. I had been out of chronic for two weeks and had spent well over a couple of thousand dollars supporting my habit. If you would have asked me then was I an addict I would have said no, boy was I wrong.

Once I got the chronic in my hand it was on, I called a couple of my main customers and picked up right where I had left off, I called my two favorite costumers, that's all it took, and everyone else would hear that I was back open for business and it was cracking. I broke down the four pounds that I had bought and got busy. By the end of the week, they were all gone. Mac liked when I ran out because he knew that I would have to help him sell his weed before he left to re-up. The only thing with Mac was that he would have so much that he wouldn't run out for months it was cool because he paid me well and still gave me fat sacks to smoke on. I wasn't working for free for anybody. I must say the people in K.C. loved chronic, Cush, Diesel or whatever you want to call it.

Tracy was kicking it with her dude Goldie by now. She came home one day and told us that she was moving out. Her guy had helped her get an apartment. I was happy for her because she was home from prison, and getting herself together, and branching out on her own. I was going to miss her being at the house, but it was time for her to do her own thing. We helped her pack her things, told her don't be a stranger, she loaded up her things and moved out, she was only twenty minutes away from us, it was all good. After a couple of months, Tabby and I also went our separate ways. I got a townhouse, and Tabby and Vickie moved together in a house. Charlie also moved off the block, I wondered if 87th and Corrington would miss us, probably not. Charlie and I moved right by each other, in a cul-de-sac, four townhouses down from one another. We all still lived close and saw each other often if not every day.

Mac had started hanging with the cats that I was leery about tough; they were going in and out of town to Super Bowls; amongst other places that I'm sure, they never had been. He took them home to Bakersfield, California to meet his family; they were bossing up. It was something about them I just didn't like, but couldn't put my hand on it something in my mind was telling me that this friendship wasn't good for Mac. I started seeing him less and less, he was always in and out of town but now even when he was in town it was straight business, and he'd be gone. I was rolling so I didn't trip I was making twenty thousand dollars every two weeks on weed. I was busy myself in and out of town from Cali to St. Louis to Atlanta. I was on the move. I had made enough money in two weeks so I had to treat myself. I brought a new three-thousand-dollar green leather sectional, with matching green leather lamps. I brought a thousand-dollar abstract painting by Peter Ketchell that I loved so much. And still, have today. Sometimes when I would be high, I would look at it and see different things. The shopping spree was great and didn't hurt my pockets at all because I could make back what I spent in two days.

Chapter 13
Homie Lover Friend

Around 1997 Lucky got out of jail from doing eight years fed time. I was happy to see him. He had lost over one hundred pounds. He went from three hundred and seventy-five pounds to two hundred and fifty pounds. He was always sexy, but now he was looking fit, and fine as hell. It seemed like all the guys that would go to prison would come out looking younger, with better bodies. Lucky was looking great I missed him a lot; after all, he helped me get my first apartment when I was young and helped me out when I first got into the game. The sex had even improved with the weight loss, and he could eat the hell out my pussy, I was super soaking his mustache. He was most definitely in the hall of fame. You would have thought that he was from Cali. with that bomb head. Lucky started right back selling dope like he wasn't on parole, but most of the men did not care that they would be leaving their families once again. Snitches were everywhere, and one was waiting to tell. He didn't think about the consequences, he loved money, and he wanted those trash bags of cash like he had before he left. We always had fun together; we would go to the club and have a ball. People said he was a rat and that he told on a few cats, but half the niggas in the town were snitches. And the ones that called him a rat were either hanging around a rat, or on themselves. I prayed that when we were together that no one tried to light his ass up because if they killed him, no matter how much love they had for me in that town, I would be a goner too.

Lucky was right back messing with all his women; I never got in my feelings we would have sex and went our separate ways. Anyway, I was feeling Richie Rich he was fine & arrogant, that's what I liked, and he was a challenge. He looked like the rapper Mace, but better damn he was sexy to me and rich, not hood rich, millionaire rich. A for real millionaire, no matter how he got it, he had it. He moved swiftly and silently; he didn't have men or women all up in his mix like the ballers that always wanted to be seen trying to gain a reputation, only to end up getting robbed or murdered. I had the biggest crush on him it was pitiful how much I liked him. He was a real sight to see; he was always alone, he had cars for days. Corvettes, Vapors, 500 Benz, trucks, he had it all, and I wanted him. I knew he was going through a divorce with his wife; he was young rich and sexy. I was feeling him; he just didn't know it though. I would see him in the club now and then he didn't come out much sometimes he would come to the club and have a drink. He made me nervous every time that I was in his presence. The times that he would be at the club, I would see him, and then he'd disappear. It was like seeing a friendly ghost. A true mystery, I dreamed about him and even prayed one time that Richie Rich would be mine.

Martez came in town on Friday to get his product and get back on the road so he could do his thing. I hooked him up with my boy that I knew had that A1 Yola. He broke me off two thousand dollars plus I had my tax of an additional five hundred dollars. After it was all said and done he still was getting a good deal because prices elsewhere were way higher.

We never had sex when we were doing deals; nothing moved but the money. Lucky was around now so I could have sex with him when I felt horny. Sex wasn't really on my mind then. I was trying to get as much money as I could because I had a lot of traveling that I was going to do that year and I needed all the cash that I could get. Martez left and made it back to St. Louis, I was relieved. I was always nervous when he left because I didn't want him to get caught and I damn sure didn't want him to say my name if he did. He was solid, but you never know who would rat you out. Later that evening Charlie, Tabby and I went to Niecy Lounge. We were going to have drinks with Tabby's new guy friend that she was hanging out with. He asked us to come out and get drunk with him; we did just that. We sat around talking almost drinking a whole fifth of Remy. Leo was telling us that he and a few of his boys were going to Atlanta next week and told us that we could go if we wanted to and that we wouldn't have to spend a dime. I was down and ready to go, Atlanta was my spot! I still would take my own cash. Tabby said that she had something to handle and that she was going to wait until Freaknik to go to Atlanta. She didn't mind me going with her dude we didn't sleep with each other's men, and if one tried to holler at us, he would most definitely get checked. We left the club loaded; Tabby left with Leo and Charlie, and I went home. That weekend I cleaned my house, took Angel out to eat at Red Lobster and shopping. Angel loved going shopping and getting new clothes; she also enjoyed money like her mom. Everyone gave her money, and she held onto it and spent ours. That Sunday we went to church, I hadn't been in a couple of months because I'd been traveling so much. I knew that I would be out of town next weekend, and needed to hear the Word! On the way to church that morning I listened to Pastor T.D. Jakes on the radio, he was talking about friends, and the message was timely. He said that confidants; you only have a few of these. They will tell you when you are wrong or right, he said confidants would be there when you are having the worst time, they will see you in the jailhouse, they will take you out the crack house, and they will always be there for you! The next type of friend he talked about was constituents. They are not into you; they are just there for what you have. Constituents will always leave you hanging when you need them the most. The third type of friend the Pastor talked about was comrades. They are not there for you or for what you have, they will team up with you, and when the job is complete they will leave you. He said to be careful who you tell your dreams to. He also said watch out for these characters in your life. I felt like my close girls were confidants. They cared for me, rode, rejoiced, and wept with me. Tabby and I loved the message; it reminded me of Shara and how she did me with Jon-Jon. Now we were going to get the good word from our Bishop two for one, and I needed all of it! Bishop spoke on just about the same message that T.D Jakes had spoken about, it was like déjà vu. He spoke from the book of Proverbs.

"Joyful who listen to me, watching for me daily at my gates, waiting for me outside my home, for whoever finds me finds life and receives favor from the lord. But those who miss me injure themselves; all who hate me love death."   Proverbs 8:33-36

The Bishop message was so good that I got up and praised the Lord, I cried out asking God for peace. I almost caught the Holy Spirit. It was working on me. After church, we went to my house; everybody came over, I cooked a huge meal. I usually cooked for at least twenty people on Sundays. Everybody loved my cooking, and everybody was eager to be at my house. I had good food and good Cali Sour Diesel. We had a great meal, we watched all the football games, and chilled. Everyone left, I cleaned and put Angel in bed and started packing for my trip coming up the next weekend.

The week went by fast, and I was ready for my weekend getaway. Leo picked me up early Friday morning, and we headed to MCI airport. We met his two homeboys at the airport they were brothers, they were sexy and light skinned. I still wasn't necessarily attracted to light skinned men but now and then one caught my eye. Their names were Moe & Lenny they had it going on in Kansas. Moe owned a car wash in K.C., he also had a big house in the ATL; I considered anything over six thousand square feet a mansion. That's where we were going to stay when we arrived. Moe also had a fat 1996 SL 500 Mercedes Benz waiting outside of Hartsfield Jackson airport for us. It was going to be one hell of a weekend. None of my girls went with me; I was with all the K.C. real players. We landed in Atlanta; I was ready to kick it. After we arrived at Moe's house we took showers and changed clothes; we got dressed quickly because everyone had a bathroom to go into at the same time, everyone was ready to get in the streets. Moe's brother, Lenny was a D- boy and couldn't wait to get on the chicks. He said that it was a lot of whores in the ATL and that he could buy some cheap head, and pussy. Moe and Leo were laid back, relaxed type guys. We went and had a late dinner at Benihana and headed out to the first club; it was called Kya. It was in midtown on Peachtree, and it was popping, but I still wanted time to fly by so that we could get to Club 112 because that was my spot and I knew that all the ballers would be there and I was trying to meet a few of them. I had a few more shots and smoked a couple of blunts with Lennie. Leo, and Moe didn't smoke I was feeling good, and the club was right.

About 1:30 am we headed out for Club 112. I was wired and ready to kick it, really, that's when the clubs started partying in Atlanta, after 1 am. We pulled up in the parking lot of the club it was crowded as usual. We valet parked and went straight through to the VIP line. Moe paid one hundred dollars for each one of us to get in. That's what all the ballers did to walk in without waiting in a long line, and we were ballers from the Midwest. When we got in Moe ordered two bottles of Dom Perignon we got a table upstairs, where the VIP section was. I immediately fired up a blunt that I had rolled up before we pulled up to the club, Biggie Smalls "I love it when u call me Big Poppa was playing, everybody downstairs on the dance floor was grooving. All the players in VIP were to fly to dance, so they were bouncing their heads up and down. The chicks were as fly as can be, everyone was Coogi down to the socks, the ambiance was lovely, and I was feeling good and confident. I fit right into the VIP section; I had on my six hundred-dollar Coogi sweater, jeans, and my Ellen Tracy shoes. I was fly no one could tell me different. I was having a ball with Leo, Moe, and Lenny. I told the guys that I was going to the restroom then walk around and check out the scene below. I went to the restroom bought some gum, and a couple of Philly blunts, that the attendant in the restroom was selling, and headed out to see what was going on in the lower level. The club was so live that all you could do was dance, I was walking and singing, and for a minute I thought I was dreaming. I closed my eyes gathering my thoughts and opened them back up to make sure that I wasn't dreaming or hallucinating. I was high but not that high; I bumped right into my mystery man Ritchie Rich. Someone told me that he had a house in Atlanta and was always there. Richie Rich was purple label Polo down with one of the iciest Rolex watches that you would ever see. I was breathless not knowing what to say. All that I could come up with was "Hey." My heart was beating fast, so many emotions took over, I was feeling optimistic, shocked, mischievous, and like a little girl. When I was around him, I turned bashful. He was so fine with skin like smooth caramel, and his eyes always hypnotized me. We had never talked back in K.C. we only waved, smiled, and kept it moving. Now we were face to face, and I didn't know what to say. He spoke, and we moved on. My heart was beating fast, but I was happy I heard his voice. He only said hey but that was a start. On my way, back to my table, some cats from Akron, Ohio stopped me one of them asked me to sip on some Cristal with them. They had a few bottles…hey this is what people did when they were on vacation. I joined them and sipped on the glass with him and his crew. After a few minutes of chilling with them I pulled out my sack rolled a blunt and started smoking. The weed would calm me and help me regain my composure back after seeing Ritchie Rich. I had bomb chronic that I brought with me. I never left home without a sack unless I was going to California. It was everywhere out there.

The Akron cats also had some super bomb Chronic, which surprised me. While I was smoking, I felt eyes on me and turned around, Richie Rich was staring me down. I already had my eyes on him from the time we bumped into each other, but somehow had lost him, like I always did. I exchanged numbers with the guy that was checking for me and headed back to my VIP section. When I got to the top of the stairs, he was standing there. He asked me, where I was going, I pointed over to the cats that I was with. He asked me for my name. Which I'm sure he already knew, I guess that's how he made conversation. I told him that my name was Queen and you are Richie Rich. He said that's your nickname what's your name! I said, Demetria, what's the difference, he responded, that he didn't want to call me what everyone else called me. He asked me why did I speak to him back in the city and run. I told him that every time that I would get the nerve to say something he would disappear. He smirked and said that's what I do. I'm a chameleon we know how to camouflage ourselves and get out of tough situations. For the rest of the night, we talked and chilled. Damn, I was in love or lust; I know it was something that I was feeling because I was floating on cloud nine, and not because of the weed. He was fine, his breath smelled good, plus, he had a lot of money, and had been my dream boy for as long as I'd known him. He was my kind of guy. I wasn't a one-night stand kind of girl, but he could've got the business right where we stood in the club! He could have got mouth lip service that night and all! After we started talking time flew by and before I knew it, it was six am. I said to him it is funny how time flies when you are having fun. Leo was ready to go; I had to tell Richie Rich goodbye. He was leaving also we exchanged numbers and went our separate ways. When the valet brought our car, we got in and pulled off. Leo was laughing he said, damn Queen you and oh boy was chopping it up, you never moved after you started talking to him. I was all smiles; they all spoke highly of him, saying that he was a baller, and they liked how he moved, I liked when men gave another hustler their props, instead of hating for no reason at all. That was a good look. All the ballers knew each other in our small town. They might not speak, but everyone knew who the heavy hitters were.

My weekend had gone even better than I thought. It would be a first that I was ready to get back to K.C.

Chapter 14
The Return of Marsha

I was glad to be back home because Marsha was returning from a federal prison in Dublin, California. I had love for her because when she got caught up with the gallons of sherm that she was caring, she never put my name in anything with the police. She told on them though, I didn't like rats, but she had got caught in the bus station with the cat, so they pretty much knew that they were together and he was involved. People would come back telling me that she said, that she had gone to prison for me. If anyone knows, people went to prison because they were doing wrong, for the love of money we will do dumb things. I wasn't getting paid for bringing drugs back, she was. It may have been my guy's drugs but, she wanted to make extra money. We all knew that we were taking penitentiary chances when we were in the streets doing wrong, and she just so had happened to get caught. She had brought the sherm back for Rashad, she didn't know his real name so she couldn't tell on him either, I had nothing but love for her, and didn't care about her telling people that it was my fault, because she was grown, and I didn't put a gun to her head, the difference was, she was a runner, and I wasn't. She did her time and was coming home.

While she was getting out, Rashad was headed to prison on his case. He received a life sentence in prison which I thought was ridiculous! Murderers didn't even get that much time. The word on the streets was, they had to mace him to get him out of the courtroom, I never asked him what happened. His mom also went to prison for money laundering. I hated that because she was so sweet and didn't deserve to be in prison, but the Government will lock you up, no matter how old you were. Marsha got in town she got dropped off at my house. I was excited to see her I welcomed her with open arms we hugged, cried and enjoyed her release. She looked wonderful; prison preserves people. Her hair was down her back, and her skin was glowing. No one would've ever thought that she had three kids because her body was banging. No stretch marks and a perfect waistline. Marsha was a true soldier; she knocked that fed time right out. We went out that night and had dinner. She had to check into the halfway house the following day so she couldn't smoke. Me, Tabby, Charlie, Vickie, Mac and his boys all went to Red Lobster. The bill came to five hundred dollars and some change. Mac paid for it all. Marsha and Mac were giving each other googly eyes before the night had ended Mac and Marsha had hooked up. A lot of chicks liked Mac. He stood around six feet five, chocolate with a body to die for. His arms were cut up, and he had a sexy, big, shiny, bald, head. He was buffed as hell and Marsha said that she was going to have him her way.

Mac helped Marsha get on her feet and told her not to ever go back to prison, and to get her life in order. At the same time, he was still trying to make-up with his wife. The one thing that I learned was men would be men. Mac was still screwing Marsha and a couple of other chicks that I knew.

It had been about a week since I had come back from Atlanta, I decided to call up Richie Rich. He told me he was up by his beauty salon off Gregory and Prospect. He had built his shop from the ground up. It was the most extravagant shop in the city. One side was for barbers, and the other side was the hair stylist. When he asked me to stop by I jumped right up, put on one of my nicest outfits, my hair always stayed on point, sprayed my best fragrance, which was, Amarige by Givenchy. I went to see him. I pulled up in my Infinity J30, thinking I was cute. He was sitting in his car, a black 500 Mercedes Benz coupe. I was checking for this cat, he was young, and fly. I wanted him and no one else. I parked my car; he told me to hop in with him. We drove down to the car wash on 59th and Prospect, he was bumping Tupac, picture me rolling, I was feeling myself, especially when we pulled into the car wash, and there was Shon and a couple of his boys. When Shon saw that it was me in the car, he mugged me down, making me lean back, and floss even harder, Ritchie observed what was going on, he had to know that I had ties to Shon the whole town knew, he turned the music up, burning rubber out of the car wash. We rode around the city, talking and sipping on Hennessey XO. I didn't drink Hennessy, but I would have drunk Seagram's Gin if he had it. We looked good together. I was Queen with the King of Kansas City, like I said, whatever I wanted I got.

After that day, we started hanging out a lot. We weren't having sex just friends. Plus, I didn't want to mess up our friendship. I would hang out with him, and he would chill out with my crew and me. Tabby would say Richie Rich was "weird, is it the money?" I didn't know, but he was my Boo.

We had been hanging out for months, it got cold outside, we had been invited to a party, it was a big one that King threw every year, and everyone would have on their finest gear. We went to the store to get outfits for the night. We needed new clothes for any event that we went to Marsha and I was on missions. Off to the mall, we went. My cousin, Dawn had on a girdle so she could steal at least ten outfits or more. She was a true booster and always looked out for everyone. Marsha went her way; she wanted to get her clothes. On our way, out the door, Marsha ended up getting caught up by the police. With Marsha getting caught up, Dawn got right out of another door. Marsha was already on parole, which turned into a parole violation, resulting in them shipping her right back off to prison. I was devastated for her, I wished we would have never gone to the mall that day, we had new outfits in our closet, but this was our lifestyle, we had a choice to do right, we didn't have any sense to change. We were always taking penitentiary chances. I was having a bad month.

The weed wasn't coming in as it should have. Chronic was out of season and wasn't in demand. Some cats in Kansas had a plug, from out west. Their weed was better than mine so sales were low and I was blowing money fast, and buying from other dealers, which wasn't cool at all.

My birthday was coming up; I had been planning a trip to Mexico, we were also going back to Freaknik, April the twenty-first. I had a busy schedule ahead of me; I was ready for the festivities. I had been staying in town taking it easy not doing much. I decided that I would throw myself, a birthday party in the park in June. I started my planning immediately; I had about five months to plan. Freaknik in April, Cancun in May and my birthday in June, they were all going to be a blast. In the process of preparing for my trip, I had received some devastating news, Shon was murdered, this had been the most fucked up news that I had received in years. He was the man that I had a love hate relationship with, no matter who I was with, he could get in my pants, I thought about all our good, and bad times throughout the years, all the times that I let him get me pregnant, resulting with me sneaking off getting abortions. I thought about the day, that he saw me, with Richie, we hadn't slept together in a while, but him being him and to let his boys, and me know that he could sleep with me when he wanted, we hooked up that night, Shon tried to knock my back out with his big anaconda saying that nigga will never fuck you as I do! He was probably correct, and he didn't have to, that's what he was for, but when the time came I would see. I thought things couldn't get any worse.

I received a call from Rashad's mom. She was a cool down to earth older lady whom I looked up too. She would give me advice, and suggestions, I would listen because I needed all the knowledge that I could get. She also knew that I loved to cook and that it was my dream to own a restaurant. I was even allowed to cook in her restaurant on different occasions when I had large orders from the Kansas City Chiefs. She would help me deliver dinners to the stadium. Sometimes she cooked for the players, and I would let her make the cash. She was a great person, but now she was in prison for money laundering from her restaurant that she owned in Kansas City, Kansas with Rashad. We were talking she said she only had eight minutes left, she asked me had I spoke with Marsha, and if I knew that Marsha was pregnant, which I didn't know she never told me anything of the sort, and we talked often. I knew that when I spoke with Marsha that she would clear this up. She hadn't been the only one to say this about Marsha. I didn't put much more thought into the situation. Marsha lied all the time. I could never tell when she was telling the truth. She said she might be lying to you, but I see her every day, and her stomach is getting big, I told moms that once she called, I would ask again, we talked about other things and hung up.

All while preparing for Shon's Home Going, I picked back up planning for my birthday so I could try and get him off my mind. I had less than four months left. It was coming fast. Through the months, Mac bought a lot of liquor for the party, and my crew boosted all the party supplies, liquor, and even some of the food. I wanted to have a Luau, a Hawaiian theme. I hired the best D.J. in town. D.J. Les could go hard on the turntables, so he was my choice. I would prepare all the side items for the feast myself. I only trusted my cooking and some of my family. After all, I was a chef, why pay someone when I was a beast in the kitchen. I hired Big Ant to work the grill because he was a grill master. My crew was going to wear hula skirts, serving fruits in watermelons hulls. It was going be the perfect set up.

The day for Shon's funeral had come, thank goodness that it didn't rain it couldn't have been any more perfect besides us burying someone we loved. The funeral was held at Lawrence A. Jones Funeral Home; it was overcrowded, it was like a club scene instead of a funeral, everyone trying to out dress each other. I would have thought that they would've had it at a huge church, but they didn't, the crazy part was, the cats that claimed that they didn't like Shon, were all in attendance, and all the women from the tri-city area. Most of the men were jealous of him because he made a major come up, or that he was screwing their chick, I always thought, why are they mad at him, check your bitch!

I had to remember a lot of niggas had more hoe in them than a chick. Shon's funeral was like a player's ball; he was Versace down, gold shades and all, holding hundreds in his hand that someone had stolen a little of before the funeral was over, scandalous, dumb ass niggas. Shon's dad was a pimp, so the funeral was real pimpish as well. Rap music was playing; Master P "Makes Them Say Uh! Na Nana", Scarface "All I Have in This World", and all the rap songs of that error, his click were drinking fifths of all types of liquor, drunk, and crying over his casket, there was at least five chicks who were pregnant claiming that he was there child's father, looking ignorant mean mugging one another, claiming to be the last one that he was with, I knew where I stood with him and his family and there was no need to be extra, we both would always love each other and would always have a bond. The funeral was popping, what snapped me back to reality letting me know that I was attending a funeral, was when I looked at the front row and saw Shon's mother, who loved him dearly, sitting there with her head down grieving for her only son. At the end of the funeral, they took Shon out to the hearse where a car show was taking place, guys were making their six fours bounce, everyone's music was playing, and everyone was smoking weed and drinking, the recession was crazy, two lines that were over a mile long, it was so long that the intercity player macs helped the two security guards stop cars from coming in between our line. Shon went out like a player, but after all, who wanted to die?

February and March had flown by so fast we had two weeks before Freaknik, everybody and their momma was smoking Chronic now. Now everyone in the city was going to Atlanta, it took them a while to catch on with what was going on out of the city, but they got with the program. I told Mac that if he took enough Chronic to Atlanta that we could double the money that we made in K.C. and triple of what it was sold for in California. Mac left for Cali so that he could ship a few pounds out to ATL. He was coming to Atlanta also, and we were about to have a ball.

My week was going well, Freaknik was five days away, and the whole city was going this year we had talked about it so much that anybody that was around us was more than likely going.

I received a call from Lucky who was still in federal prison that messed up my whole day. I asked him how he was doing. He was ok; he said he had lost fifty pounds and was getting his mind and body right. He asked me how I was doing. I told him that I was ok and was heading down to Atlanta. He told me to make sure that I took plenty of pictures, he then asked me to send him naked pictures as well, he told me to play with my pussy and get it wet, and play with my nipples to make them hard, I told him hell no, I didn't do shit like that, he responded, that he couldn't tell that I didn't send naked flicks, because I had sent some to Rashad, he said, "and that nigga showed me, so if he showed me, and he knows I fuck with you, I can imagine who else has seen that juicy pussy." He smirked through the phone. I felt humiliated, but still downplayed the conversation I said, what are you talking about, as if I didn't know. He replied, "I went thru CCA and Rashad was there." I replied so what does that mean? He responded, "you sent him naked pictures, and he showed me but you can't send me any?"

He then said, "you're going to sit here and lie to me saying that you don't do that bullshit, well I see differently, plus I know what your pussy looks like, inside and out, I know that pussy from anywhere." I was furious and lost for words. I didn't know what to say because I knew that I had sent the pictures to Rashad. I knew one more thing, I would never, ever send naked pictures to another man in jail again; maybe some lingerie but naked, please, never. I couldn't believe that

Rashad was showing my goods to the cats in jail. I thought about the pose, my legs were wide open, trying to satisfy him while he was gone, and here he was displaying my goods. Lucky said that he wasn't tripping, but he wanted some pictures too. He was tripping. I told him that I would send him some just to get him off my case, he would never receive them.

Mac went back to the west coast to re-up. He said that he was going to bring back at least thirty to fifty pounds of the best Cush that the Bay area had. Mac had a hell of a plug on the weed and the white, but I stuck to the weed.

I was so ready to get to Atlanta that I couldn't think straight. I hadn't seen my brother J. Bo in a while. We planned on hooking up in the ATL and paint the town. J. Bo had connections; I knew being with him we could Boss Up and walk straight in the clubs with not one issue. I liked that kind of treatment and had got accustomed to the lifestyle.

J. Bo still lived in St. Louis he also had a house in Atlanta. Once we arrived, we were going to be going straight to his house for a smoke session and maybe hit him up for a little cash. My homies had love for me, even though I had money they had much more, I felt if they could give money to hoes and tricks that thought two and three hundred dollars was something, sometimes not getting get shit, but some dick, they just wanted to say that they had been with a boss, being degraded, the homies damn sure was going to give me something because we made things happen together.

Mac also had a couple of pounds that J. Bo had ordered. It would arrive the same day that we got to the A. It was going to be coming straight to the hotel. Not my hotel for sure. I wasn't down with the get the package shit that was just like being a mule.

I was so ready to get out and get it in, I was single and ready to mingle a one-night stand, or something was just what the doctor ordered, but for some reason, it wasn't happening. I felt freaky; after all, it was Freaknik, and I was going to get my freak on.

We had two days left before our trip. J.C. came over and drove Charlie, Tabby and I to the mall. I always took J.C. with me, he was my little play brother, and he would help me pick out my outfits. He was very blunt and outspoken he also had pretty good taste. I loved J.C. and was still praying that he stopped smoking sherm. He had started smoking it and couldn't stop. He still kept himself up, kept a bankroll, but the drugs were frying his brain.

After we shopped, we picked up our rental car out at the airport. We got it for two weeks just in case we stayed longer than we planned. On the way home from getting the rental car I had been thinking about what Lucky had told me about Rashad. I needed to free my mind, so I decided when I got home I would write him a letter and tell him how I felt about him showing my pussy to niggas, and niggas he probably didn't know, when I got home I immediately grabbed a notebook and a pen; I couldn't get what Lucky had said off my mind. I had been upset about it since he said that to me about those pictures, and writing was the only way to free my mind. I knew that's how jail went. I even heard stories about how dudes in jail would get money by selling naked pictures of women. Rashad wasn't broke, but he was damn sure showing off my goods and to people I knew.

Dear Shad;

How are you doing? How is everything going down your way? As for me, I'm ok, I'm going to Atlanta for Freaknik this weekend, but before I leave for the trip I had something's on my mind I wanted to let you know how I'm feeling. Lucky called me the other day, he told me, while he was passing thru Leavenworth he saw you, and you showed him naked pictures of me. The one question that I have for you is why would you show him pictures of me? You claim that I'm your girl, and you love me, but you are in there showing off my pussy! How many guys have you shown my pictures to? I know one thing you made me open my eyes, and trust me it will never happen again!!! This is a lesson for me, and I know that men in jail are no better than the men on the streets. All you guys do is tell us what we want to hear, but I'm not with it. I still have love for you but your actions were unacceptable, and I feel you owe me an apology. That's all I wanted to say because it was on my mind and I haven't been sleeping well. I'm wondering, how many cats in there have seen my pussy? I'm sure if I know any more of them, they'll be trying to holler at me, thanks to you! I'll have a lot of prison pen pals. Write me back; I'm dying to hear what you have to say, whatever you say, please keep it one hundred.

One love!

Demetria

I felt so much better after I had written the letter. Now it was time to pack my bags and get ready to party.

Chapter 15
Freaknik

We loaded up the car up, and we were out. We made sure that we had our Tupac, E40, Luther and most definitely Gerald Levert CDs. We always left on Thursdays so that we could arrive Friday morning. Mac was back and ready to go. The weed had already been sent to Atlanta and would arrive in the morning to one of the hotels in Midtown. It didn't matter what hotel it was arriving to, it wasn't my business, and I didn't want to know. Mac had already sent a chick from Cali to handle the situation. I just needed it to touch down and get into my hands; then it was a done deal. I was ready to work and play. The two always worked very well for me.

We got to the ATL and checked into a new hotel called the Grand Hotel. On 14th St. it was an extravagant five-star hotel. There were already people everywhere. It wasn't even noon, and it was going down. No sooner than we checked in, we were back out in the streets. Mac was staying in another hotel with his boys; I would give him a few hours then getting with him so he could get all his business straight.

Tabby rolled up a few blunts, we smoked a couple and headed out to see what was going on in the Atl. Tabby and I had to smoke a blunt before we did anything, we called it miracle marijuana. It took all your worries, headaches, and heartaches away, shit it was a habit that we didn't want to shake. We were crewed up; it was me, Tabby, Charlie, Vickie, Shanna, and Tracy. Shanna was my homegirl from back in the day we still hung out on special occasions and this weekend was most definitely a special occasion.

Cats were walking all around with snakes on their necks; this was the new fad, and several men had them, I had enough snakes in my life, so

I didn't want to pet or play with theirs. This year was wild but nothing compared to the years before. I'm sure some chicks left not knowing who the father of their child was, or how they'd wake up with another woman in the bed. The security guard said that it had become so out of control last year that they had to change some things up and make it better. It wasn't better because I liked all the cats taking out their dicks swinging them around without a care in the world, even the little dick dudes were slanging theirs around, what a delirious site to see, but not this year the city of Atlanta did not have it. It didn't matter to me I was there to shop, go to the clubs and sell my weed.

We stood outside our hotel and fired up a blunt, and that was all she wrote, cats were ready to burn, and I had what they needed. Everywhere I went I sold sacks of seven grams or better that meant if you didn't have two hundred and fifty dollars or better keep it moving. All the guys were buying the good Cush; they had come to have fun and spend money. The Chronic was a great investment for everyone, and if I got caught up, I wouldn't be doing federal time. We loved Atlanta, it was the only city that I had been to where you could smoke weed like you were at home, but in the club, Cali had the bomb everywhere, but even there I couldn't smoke like I did in the A. And everybody smoked. Chronic was the new ballers high. I was sure to make five thousand dollars off the sacks, and I was going to make an additional thousand on the two pounds that J. Bo was going to grab from Mac. We showed him straight love on the price. Six, thousand dollars was good money to go home with while you were really on vacation kicking it instead of working.

Everywhere we went Tabby fired up a blunt exhaling so everyone could smell it, we were boss chicks bossing up just like the men. It wasn't to gain clientele, nor attention it's what we did and how we smoked. The aroma was the trap. They would smell the great scent and follow their noses, bait. I loved my job and was damn good at what I did.

We had a great day, but now it was time for the Hotlanta nightlife. I had already sold over a pound of weed in the mall and streets, and we hadn't been in town for twenty-four hours. I knew in the club that I would rack up we were going to Club 112, where we knew all the ballers would be, they didn't even count how much they spent in the club they just wanted to play as hard as they could, and stunt on the next set of ballers.

I met up with Mac and J. Bo, off the 10th Street at the gas station. Mac told me to count the cash that J. Bo had handed me; I knew I didn't have to count it, but I did, it was all there, and I gave J.Bo his pounds, I told him that we would hook up later after the club. He said that he might sell one of them and that he and his boys were going to smoke on the other one. He is a true definition of a baller he wasn't buying ounces of exotic to smoke on; he was smoking on pounds before he was ever with the Mob.

When we arrived at Club 112 the line at the door was ridiculous. There were celebrities everywhere, Allen Iverson was newly famous and had just nabbed a deal with Reebok. Everyone was on his dick… niggas that swore they were bosses were acting like groupies. He was young, and chicks were trying to be his girl. I was looking for a D-boy, so I never tried to get with athletes, besides most of them liked white girls and I was chocolate, with gold teeth in my mouth.

As soon as we walked in we went straight into the VIP section; the world was so small because if you were on the level that I was on, you were bound to bump into to someone from every state. I ran right into Martez. He was standing out like a sore thumb, looking sexy as hell with his luscious lips; he was with his brother and the rest of his St. Louis, and E. St. Louis boys. He asked me to give him a blunt for his boys, so they can see the difference from the dirt that they should have never fired up in a club! Martez didn't smoke; he popped bottles like they were water. While we were standing there talking, I fired up a blunt, as fast as I fired it up, I had sacks sold. I told the two cats that wanted to purchase it that I had to go downstairs and get it from my people. I didn't want Martez to see me making moves in the club, or to know how much weed I had because I was about to hit him up. I would be asking Martez could I have some money to buy a pair of shoes from the mall tomorrow, not just any pair, but a pair that would cost a pretty penny. He reached into his pocket and pulled out stacks of hundred-dollar bills. I was hoping that he would give me one thousand dollars. He gave me six hundred; I was good with that, I was coming up this whole trip and wasn't going to be greedy. After he gave me the cash, I told Martez that I would talk to him later. There were chicks all around his table, and I wasn't trying to cock block I just wanted some money. Martez said that we would hook up later which I knew was a negative; he was doing his thing and had bad chicks all around him, and I was with my crew, and we were doing us. I knew I wouldn't see or hear from him until I got back to K.C.

As usual, Freaknik was fun, but it was time to get back home. On the way back to the city, I received a call from prison, it was Marsha, she asked about the trip. I told her about how our wild weekend turned out then I told her that I had been receiving calls from people that were locked up with her, and they were telling me that she was pregnant. She became very defensive and said that they were lying and whoever it was needed to keep her name out of their mouth and mind their business. I asked her why people would lie on her like that. She said that the city was full of haters and that they loved spreading rumors. She changed the subject and asked about Mac. I told her that I had just been with him and that he was good.

She asked me did we take a lot of pictures. I told her that we did and that I would send her some as soon as I touched down in K.C. I always sent pictures to my people in jail; it meant a lot to them. They said it helped them do their time if they could see friendly faces. It seemed like all my people were dying or going to jail. I had been to two funerals that year, and it was only April.

Cats were robbing everybody, and if you had over five thousand dollars, you were a target. These were petty robbers looking for any kind of come up that they could get. It would be three or four people splitting five thousand dollars. People like Turk would rob cats for their Rolex, cash, and clothes. He had just hit Richie Rich up for over one hundred and fifty thousand dollars and a couple of Rolex watches. Word on the street was that one night he followed Richie Rich home and started watching his spot and one night he went in and found the money. Richie found out it was Turk and put a hit out on him. Turk was treacherous and didn't care; the sad part was, the more people he robbed, the less money he had. As I say, robbers never prosper. Turk had even started going to different states with the cats that he robbed jewelry on, hanging out at clubs then he would get friendly with the cats that had money and befriend them. Because he was just as icy, they jumped right on his bandwagon, not knowing what they had coming to them. He would then get into their homes and steal everything that they had.

Turk was scandalous as hell. One day he came to our house to buy some clothes for his kids from Tracy, she had a few trash bags of clothes that she had lifted from Dillard's. He asked to use our bathroom we let him not thinking he would be on some scandalous shit. And just that fast he had pulled a move on us. He came out of the bathroom grabbed his trash bag and left. The other bag that wasn't his was also gone, but we watched him take his one bag, now everyone was looking for this big bag of clothes that had just disappeared right before our eyes... We were all sitting there stunned trying to figure out what happened knowing the bag was just sitting in our face. Tracy was aggravated because she had two four-hundred-dollar orders in that bag. We thought back from what happened in the last ten minutes and figured it out, Turk had pulled the bag into the bathroom right under our nose with his scandalous ass. He took the clothes and threw them out the window. As soon as we figured it out, we ran down the street to his house and confronted him. Of course, he denied it and said we were crazy and he didn't have shit of ours. We told his slum ass that we were not leaving until he gave us the clothes, after about ten minutes of arguing with him he finally threw the bag of clothes out of the door and called us some scandalous bitches, Tracy said no you didn't you sorry ass pussy! Coming down to our house stealing our shit I should call my boys to come and whip your scandalous ass! You gonna steal from some girls. She was hot, and so were we. We all were ready to fight his big ass. After we got the bag of clothes back we laughed at his foul ass the rest of the day; he was cold busted, we wasn't have it.

I was still hanging with Richie Rich, my crew and I would hang with him and have a good time. He was still mad about Turk hitting him up, but it wasn't that big of a deal. He had so much money that what Turk had got wasn't shit it was just the principle. I asked Richie did he want to go to Cancun in a couple of weeks with the girls and me. King was also going with us, and with King around, I wouldn't have to spend a lot of money. King always took care of me. Richie said that he had business to take care of that weekend in the South Padre Islands.

Chapter 16
Cancun, Mexico

It was just about time for the Cancun trip and me, and my girls were ready to get it in. Mac and I had gone through fifty pounds of Chronic form April to May. Things were looking good, and the money was right. I made seventy-five thousand dollars during that month. These were great numbers for only selling weed, and I was ready to spend a little. I called the Versace store in New York and ordered a couple of swimsuits, a Versace beach bag, and Versace shades. I was ready for whatever. It was going to be a week to remember. As the old saying goes, what goes on in Cancun stays in Cancun. Tabby and Tracy were getting ready also. A few of our girls that we hung out with were going with us also. We were deep and ready to do the damn thing in Mexico.

I started driving Tracy and Abbie to the malls. Abbie wasn't going to Mexico but she was a big help in the malls since she was white, she could carry out the biggest Dillard's or Jones store bag without anyone looking at her. Tracy loaded two of Dillard's biggest bags with all swimsuits and the others with all the clothes that we had picked out. Plus, Vickie worked in Dillard's and would call us when she was working alone. She worked in all the departments, so all the kids and adults were well taken care of. We went to two different malls, and at the end of the day they had lifted over six thousand dollars' worth of clothes for us, and to sell. We were going to take all the swimsuits that we didn't want to Cancun and sell them. We were ready to go.

The next morning Tracy called, she was crying hysterically. I asked her what was wrong. She said her mom had just called and told her that her brother had been murdered. All I could do was just drop my head and pray. I had already been two a few funerals and didn't want to go to anymore. I felt so bad for Tracy and her family. I wanted to hug her. Her little brother had a twin, and that made it even worse.

I told her that I would meet her at her mother's house and headed out. When we arrived at Tracy's mom's house everyone was crying and very upset, the twin was doing the worst he was hurt and couldn't think. The girls and I hugged him and told him God was going to take care of everything. He didn't want to hear anything about God right then. All he wanted to do was find the cats that killed his twin brother. We asked Tracy what happened; she told us that her younger brother had got into it with an older guy. They were arguing, and the guy shot and killed him. She was so upset, and I felt her pain. I hadn't had a family member being killed before, but I knew it hurt like hell. I had been to a lot of funerals, and it was beginning to be too much.

We had three weeks until Cancun, and now this was happening. Tracy said that she might not be going now because it was so much going on. I wanted her to go, but I understood. Tracy, Tabby and I always traveled everywhere together, and I was going to miss her. She had already paid for her trip, and I was hoping she could get some of her money back if she decided not to go. The funeral would be next week, and we would be by her side to support her and her family.

It is said that death comes in threes and I was beginning to believe it because a few days after Tracy's brother was murdered we received a call from Omaha that our cousin Lil' T had been murdered. It was so crazy because no one in our family had ever been murdered before. The people in our family died of old age, and now it was murder, now we would have to take a trip to Omaha. Two funerals in 10 days and a trip to Mexico in three weeks!

I spoke with my cousin Sylvia and asked her what had happened to Lil' T? She said that he had started selling drugs and that he was staying over in South Omaha with one of our other cousins. The cats from South Omaha was beefing with him because he was making more money than them. They didn't want him on their turf, and then there was a confrontation that leads up to the shooting and killing him in front of my other cousins. I felt terrible for Sylvia and my family. It was most definitely time to pray.

"Dear God,

I am on my knees asking you to help my family in this time of sorrow, also please bless Tracy and her family. I know we do wrong, but we are asking you for your forgiveness, guidance, and strength. Please forgive me for all my sins and wrongdoing. I need you right now to shower your blessings on our families and bring us better days. We love you, Lord, I love you, and I'm nothing without you, I ask that you bring joy, in the name of Jesus I pray Amen."

We attended Tracy's brother's funeral that next Wednesday and then we would have to drive to Nebraska that Friday to go to Lil' T's funeral on Saturday. Tracy said she was going to go with us to support us. We always had each other back and would continue to. I loved my girls we had a down ass click the way homegirls and family were supposed to be.

J.C. let me drive his car to Omaha. It was an old-school Delta 88 fixed up with Dayton's and Vogues, with candy burgundy paint. The cats in Omaha loved the car; they drove long old school Electra 225's. I hated those long cars they drove, a few cats had it going on, but Omaha was country as hell, but it was my hometown. Lil' T's funeral was so sad; my cousin presided over the funeral; he made everyone feel better. The good thing about being family was that they were mostly all church people and they stayed praying for us, and that's what we needed prayer warriors covering us. Sylvia was so depressed; we tried to comfort her as much as we could.

After the funeral, we headed back to K.C. Tracy decided to go ahead and go to Cancun. I was glad because we all needed a vacation and it was going to be beautiful.

I was so glad that the weekend was over and we had gotten through both funerals.

My swimsuit and bag had been delivered from the Versace store. I was feeling ecstatic and ready for my trip now. I tried on my swimsuit; it fit perfect. It was black and white with the Versace Medusa heads on the buttons. I knew I was going to catch something and I wasn't talking about a cold either. It was about to go down next week; someone one was going to get some friendly pussy.

Mac told me that I had been slacking on my weed sells and he needed me to help him get his last seven pounds sold so he could go and get a new batch. That wasn't going to be an issue at all. I called a Kansas cat he grabbed four of the pounds for six thousand a piece, and I broke the other three down so I could make extras for my trip. The three pounds were gone in exactly four days; I had three more days before I left for Cancun. I packed my last few things and dropped Angel to her aunts and got ready for my vacation.

Thursday took forever to come but it was finally here, and we were ready to head out. It was about eight females with us; King was the only guy. We loaded our bags into the car and headed to the airport. On the way to the airport, I stuffed the ounce of marijuana that I was taking with me. I knew I could get it to Mexico I just couldn't bring any back through customs because they didn't play that.

We got to the airport, and everyone was there, Tabby, Tracy, D.J., Jazz, Coco, Sheila, King and myself. We were ready for whatever, we boarded and was off to Mexico. When we got to Houston, we changed planes from a regional jet to a big ass plane. We had a ball laughing on the plane, the St. Lunatics and Nelly were on our flight, they were entertaining the whole plane with jokes, it was like Soul Plane, sixty percent of the people were black. King had fallen asleep and kicked off his shoes and had the whole plane smelling like Chronic. He had got comfortable and forgot that he had a bag of Chronic in his sock.

We laughed and woke him up; I told him to put his shoe back on before we all ended up in jail. He laughed and put his shoes back on and went back to sleep. The plane was so crunk that I couldn't sleep. I was too excited; this Puff Daddy All-Star weekend was going to be the greatest!

When we arrived in Cancun, we went to our rooms and immediately headed to the action. We knew we wouldn't be doing much sleeping on this trip. We were there to have fun not sleep. As I always said nothing comes to a sleeper but a dream. We fired up a blunt, and we were ready for to party. We started seeing our Cali people; everyone that was somebody was there. J. Bo and his St. Louis boys were there with some cats from Detroit. The Black Mafia Family was in the building; they were a bunch of rich niggas. Every rapper that you wanted to see was in attendance; the first night we were there, we went to a party where Jermaine Dupree was the D.J... He had the party going so crazy; we popped bottles of Dom Perignon all night. We partied until six in the morning and were back up and out in traffic before Friday at noon.

We hung out and did some shopping; we went into the Gucci store, Tracy and Jazz bought a pair of shoes. It was so crowded that Tracy hit the Gucci store up for a bad ass white swimsuit that she was going to wear on Saturday. We laughed because she caught them slipping. We were having the time of our lives meeting new people and chilling with the ones we already knew. Coco had been checking Nelly from the St. Lunatics out the whole time; she said before we left she would be hooking up with him. Tabby had met a guy from Denver. He was tall, sexy, and looked like a businessman. I hadn't seen anyone who had caught my eye yet. All the cats were looking good, but I was waiting on the one that made me say "he can get the business."

Friday night we went to a party where Biz Markie was the D.J. It was even better than the night before. We partied so hard and met so many new people, the weather was beautiful, and everyone was having a great time. D.J. met a guy and left with him, all the rest of us were partying like rock stars. We didn't get in until Saturday morning at eight is. I had a few numbers that I had gotten a few cats but nothing that made me say, WOW.

Tabby had seen her Denver man when we got back out on Saturday. She went and had lunch with him. When she came back, we headed to the K.C. and JoJo shake that ass contest, at Super Splash. The crowd was ridiculous, and the strippers were the shit. The winner would receive five thousand dollars, and the girls were getting loose as a goose. Some chick name Sugar and White Chocolate from Atlanta won. They both made their ass talk, while they did a routine like they were eating each other out. The cats were going wild. After we left the booty shaking contest, we headed to the bar where we met some Texas cats. They all were fly as hell. We were checking them all out, and every one of them could have gotten the business from us. Their names were E, Lex, and Big D. They were all drinking on small bottles of purple something that I had never seen. I asked them what were they drinking on, they said its' called Syrup, and we are not drinking we spin on it. They asked us did we want to try it out. Tabby and I said yes and tried it out. Within the hour of sipping the syrup, I was high as hell, feeling different. They said that the bar would put me to sleep if I didn't keep it moving. I didn't want to go to sleep, it was cracking on the island, so I didn't ask for any more of the grape ape as Lex called it. We chilled with the Texas cats for a while. Jazz started hollering at Lex, he was a sexy, big boy, my type of hustler, it was written all over his face, but Jazz had already got on him plus, I could tell that he was arrogant as hell, throwed in the game, in Texas slang. He had on his icy jewels with some wood frame, diamond out Cartier shades, with the Presidential Rolex watch. He was looking big and sexy. They were all cool, but it was just something about the cat Lex I liked maybe it was his arrogance, I couldn't figure it out. Even King was hanging out with them. We were sitting around chatting when this cat walked pass with his girl; he was so fine and dressed to impress. I told Tabby that I wanted him. When I finally found what, I liked he had to be with a chick. We gave each other eyes the whole time that we were at the bar. I couldn't stop looking at him, and I didn't care if his girl saw me looking. She wasn't my friend so I was looking and she had better stay by his side because if he was alone, I was going to step to him. That was something I didn't do, but he was the man for me while I was on this island.

We exchanged numbers with the Texas cats and were ready to get dressed for Puff Daddy's All-White party that was taking place at a hotel later that evening. We knew that it would be the best party of the trip. That's what we came for, no matter where Puff Daddy had a party it went hard. I had been to a couple of his parties in Atlanta, and New York and they were always off the chain, Puff knows how to do it.

We went back to the hotel where we met four ladies from France. They were on vacation having a good time. We showed them all the swimsuits that we brought to sell. They tried them on and bought seven swimsuits. Tracy and I split the money and started getting dressed. I was wearing a white Coogi dress with some cream Via Spiga pumps. I knew I was going to be looking good. I had long, wavy, beach ready weave in my hair, and I made sure I swung it like it was mine. I shined up my diamonds in my gold teeth and was ready to play. Tonight, I would find someone that caught my eye. I bought a sexy fragrance at the mall called Cancun that smelled so sexual. Everyone in my crew was looking, and smelling like a million bucks. King had on his Versace shirt and slacks looking real fly, he was the true definition of his name, the Godfather. We were ready to do what we do all over again; party, party, party!!

When we arrived, there were so many people everywhere trying to get in. We had purchased platinum packages for all the events for the entire week, so we didn't have to wait in the long lines. We walked straight into everything. When we got in King ordered three bottles of

Dom Perignon, and we started drinking. Puffy was walking around he also was the D.J. at the party. It was one of the best parties that I had ever been too. I met two cats that I exchanged numbers with; I had a couple of shots of tequila with one of them. After my second shot I looked up, the cat that I was checking out earlier who was with his broad, was walking in with her following behind. He spotted me as well; it was as if we were the only two in the room at that moment. I was right back on him, and he was checking for me also. I left out and went to the bathroom to see if I was looking good. I was flyer than a helicopter; no one could tell me anything. When I walked out the bathroom the cat was standing right there. He said, I saw you checking for me earlier ma, and we meet again. I responded to him that he had to be checking me back out for him to see all that. He said that he was, he asked me my name I told him, Queen. I asked him his; He said his name was Markel and that he was from West Philly. He was fine standing well over six feet tall, two hundred pounds of chocolate, with a great body and a nice lineup, his barber did him well, and so did his mother and father. His breath was minty… a man with fresh breath and good smelling cologne turned me on. I usually went for heavier men, but he caught my eye off the top. Markel said well you know I brought sand to the beach so I should go, but I'm shaking her after the party and you're going with me. I shook my head and said that's a shame. He said it is, what it is. I was down and ready to be bad.

All night I thought about Markel, was I finally going to have a one-night stand? Yep, I was ready to see him. Tabby was leaving the club with the Denver cat that she had met and Coco had gotten with Nelly. She said she was going to have him and she did. D.J. was with the guy that she had met the night before at the club, and they were in love like they had known each other all their lives. It was cute; everyone had hooked up with someone. I had never had a one-night stand, but tonight in Cancun I was thinking long and hard about it. About an hour before the party was over I saw Markel's girl leaving. He shook her just like he said he would; I thought to myself that men weren't shit; look how he got rid of her to get with me. After she left, he came right over to the table with my crew and me and started drinking and lounging with us as he had never been there with a woman. I really knew how to pick them. They were never any good for me but that's how I played, I wanted a challenge. Like Snoop Dog said, "We don't love these hoes" that's exactly how I felt about them. We took a few shots, he whispered in my ear, telling me how he wanted to taste me, and that he wanted me to leave with him. He sure knew how to get me aroused, because as bad as I wanted him, I wouldn't be making the first move. I told King that I was going to grab some breakfast with Markel and I would meet back up with them at the all-night spot that we hung out at ever since we got there. It was two am, and the fun was just beginning.

Markel and I headed out; we took a taxi to his hotel or someone's hotel because his chick was nowhere around. Once we got inside of the taxi, our real fun began, Markel started kissing all over my neck then he sucked on my earlobes, which had me extremely aroused. I was high, and feeling tipsy from all the bubbly, and the shots that I had drank. As he sucked on my neck he went under my mini Coogi dress, pulled my thong to the side and started playing with my warm wet pussy; he teased my clitoris making me swarm. It felt so good, that I relaxed and let go, after all, I was on vacation. After kissing on my neck, and playing in my puddle, he went straight down and started eating my pussy right in front of the taxi driver. I was embarrassed at first because the taxi driver was looking through his rearview mirror, but then I thought, we're in Cancun and what happens in Cancun stays in Cancun, and if it didn't matter who cared? Not me. Markel had a mean head game; he was putting his tongue so far up my pussy, that he was making me buck, I enjoyed getting tongue fucked. I held onto the back of the seat and the front seat, while he broke me off until I had an eruption, right in the back of the cab. He had to be the bomb because I didn't get cum often, I thought, only Lucky could make me squirt like this. I know the taxi driver had to have a hard-on just from the way Markel had me moaning, with so much passion, shit he probably busted a nut in his shorts. When we arrived at the hotel I told him that if he wanted to have sex, he would have to pay me, even though I wanted him, he wasn't about to get it for free, he already knew how I tasted and he wanted more. He asked me how much I was charging him; I told him that I wanted five hundred dollars. He said that he would give me four hundred. I was cool with that because I wanted him just as bad as he wanted me. The way he munched on my pussy and made me feel exuberant, he could have got it for free, but he bit the bait, and it was on. He pulled out his condoms; we got right to it, he already had me wet as a river, we banged one another out, his sex was just as magnificent as his head. When I say bomb, that's what he was. He beat it up, flipped me over, hitting it doggy style, smacking my ass like he had been knowing me and what I liked all his life. I threw it back at him, making sure I pleasured him and myself, tightening every muscle that I had on his dick then releasing, it, my pussy had its own heartbeat. He said that my pussy was, grabbing, and gripping his dick like I was sucking it. We had twenty-five minutes of all types of position fucking. He couldn't handle me, yelling out like he was King Kong! He finished, then shook and shivered like a wounded dog. That meant he was satisfied and got his money's worth in my eyes; I know I did. After he finished, we lay there catching our breath for a couple of minutes; he told me that my pussy was so good, he said it was explosive, then continued to tell me that his boy was next door in a room and he would give me four hundred more dollars to fuck him also. He said you could even get the five. I laughed and told him I would call one of my girls, but I wasn't doing that. I was already on some hoe shit, but it wasn't even in my blood to screw another man that I didn't know, especially that I had never seen or wasn't attracted to. I had come to kick it not sell my goodies, I told him. I was kind of embarrassed that he had asked, but that's how the game was. I was a hustler and not a whore, but he wasn't wrong for asking after all I had friends that got gangbanged by clicks for money, that just wasn't me. I wanted him, not his boy after we finished screwing; I washed up, left my wet thong in the restroom, jumped in a taxi and went back to the meeting spot where King and the girls were. I walked up like I had been to breakfast and back. I'm sure they could see the glow on my face because he made me feel brand new. I lied by omission saying that I was going to breakfast, after all, I was breakfast for Markel because he had eaten well and I made sure that he had gotten full! He chewed and swallowed. We never even exchanged numbers so I would probably never see him again. King didn't know that it was a lot of sex going on right under his nose. On the other hand, we were like his little sisters, so he just didn't trip he knew that his angels were little demons. We were all getting our freak on we had friendly pussy that weekend. We laughed about it and kept having the good time that we were having.

Before we packed up to leave from our vacation Tabby went one last time to see her Denver dude to say good-bye. When she came back she was laughing; she said bitch you are not going to believe this, I said believe what? She said I've been fucking a US Marshall. I said you did what, and when? She said that the Denver dude was a police officer and he said he didn't tell her because he knew she wouldn't have hooked up with him. We laughed so hard, I told her well we blew a whole lot of weed smoke in his face while we were smoking and he didn't mind. She said, and he blew a whole lot of smoke up my ass, and I didn't mind either. We laughed like hell at Tabby. I told her that I knew he was to clean cut and that I just thought that he was a businessman. He was more than a businessman he was the law getting his freak on in Cancun.

Everyone had a one-night stand that weekend but Tracy, Jazz, and King. The rest of us had done something strange for a little change, wild and it was fun. I didn't have a problem with what I had done. I enjoyed it and had no regrets.

It was time to get back to K.C. and plan my birthday party and chill with the kids; I had to make up for being absent.

We boarded a plane and headed home. When we arrived in Houston to change planes, the customs agents took me through a whole different line from everyone else. I didn't know what was going on. I made sure I didn't have any weed on me. I was on probation and had permission to leave the country, but for some reason, they were snatching me up. When I got to the back room, I gave them my travel permit and asked them what did I do? They said that I had a warrant out of Clay County, Missouri for checks. Someone had stolen my checks earlier in the year and used them up, but it wasn't me. I explained to them that I had to get a hand writing exemplary and that my probation officer was aware of all of this. They checked my paperwork out for about an hour, seeing that I had permission to be out of the country. I missed my connecting flight. They finally let me go after my story checked out. Now I would be stuck in Houston's airport for the next three and a half hours alone because all my girls had flown home. While I was walking around buying souvenirs I met a guy that worked at the airport. We chatted, he was cool, he said that he was getting off in twenty more minutes and we could have a drink at his apartment. He lived right by the airport and would bring me back in time for my flight. When he got off, we went to his crib and had a drink. I may have been tripping, but I went. He also had some good weed; we smoked after we got high he started talking like he wanted to hook up. He wasn't my type, and I didn't date men that had jobs that didn't make much. I told him to take me back the airport because he didn't have anything coming from me. He took me back I said thanks and headed to my gate. When I arrived at my gate, my whole crew was still there waiting for me, which made me smile. I told them I thought that they had left, so I left with the old boy and chilled, Tabby said girl you are a damn fool, we came together, and we weren't leaving until we knew you were cool, that was loyalty.

We boarded our plane and headed to Kansas City, upon arrival things looked strange; there were police waiting outside our gate. I saw one of them mouth the number eight six. I had on a Reebok short set with the number eight six on it; they were waiting for me. I walked out, and they immediately arrested me for the check warrant. Customs back in Houston let me go but called Clay County, and they were waiting. I went to jail and had a twenty-five-thousand-dollar bond; I was there for a day and a half getting processed in. I couldn't wait to get out. King went and paid twenty-five hundred dollars to get me out through a bail bondsman and never asked me for a dime of it back. He always helped me out. I loved my big brother! All my play brothers loved me and did anything for me. But the international player Mac had my back. I got out and still had my beautiful Cancun tan. I got home took a long hot bubble bath and waited on Angel's aunt to bring her home so we could lie around for the evening. I sat in the hot bubbly water smiling and thinking about how great of a week we had. We had the time of our lives as we would always say on our extravagant outings. Angel's aunt brought her home, we gave each other a big hug, ordered pizza, I gave her, the souvenirs I brought her and laid on the sofa watching movies and eating pizza for the rest of the night.

Chapter 17
Party Planning

It was time to start back planning for my birthday party. We had planned just about everything out. I decided I was going to hire D.J. Les to get the party right; he was the best D.J. in K.C. Charlie, Vickie, Trecie, and Tabby would serve drinks or fruit from a watermelon. Tracy would help me greet people. I ordered two kegs of beer from Joe Looney's liquor store on 39th and Prospect and told them that we would pick them up on the day of the party. I didn't eat pork anymore so all the food that would be served would be beef, turkey, fish, and chicken.

We had already gone to the party stores and snatched up anything with a Hawaiian theme to it. We had bought a thousand dollars' worth of food stamps. That would be more than enough food for everyone to get a couple of plates. We were going in for the party, and my crew helped me out in every way that they could.

Mac returned with some of the best buds that northern California had. I knew we wouldn't be running out until July. He came back with an eighteen-wheeler full of weed. It was fifty pounds of Cali love. He said he tried to get more, but that's all that they could supply him with. That was a lot a weed for it to be Chronic because you couldn't get a lot of chronic like you could regular weed. Had he been getting Bobby Brown he could have bought thousands of pounds at a time, but with the exotic, you could only get so much, and he bought all that they had.

I had one week to go before the party, so I decided to go to L.A. for a little pre-birthday trip. I took my mom, and my girl Renee came with us. Renee was my girl, she was a hustler like the rest of us and a sweet person, but piss her off, and she was sure to get in your ass. We had a ball in Cali, we checked into the residence inn, and then shopped all day. After eating Roscoe's Chicken and Waffles, we dropped ma dukes off for the night, and we went over to the homies Swany Mack's place to smoke out and talk some business about getting some bud to K.C. I had known Swany from when he used to come to K.C. with Chico, and we remained good friends. When I was in Cali, I always stopped by to hang out with Swany Mac off th and Budlong. He lived in between the blood and the Crips but I never knew what side he was representing and I liked that.

We left Swany and went to Shona's hood off 77th and Raymond, 74 Hoover was what they claimed, everywhere we went in Cali they were smoking good bud. I didn't have to buy any because they all gave me sacks when I came in town. It was nothing but Cali love, and I loved that Cali bud. The weed was my man, and that's the only man I claimed. Shona was going to meet us at her cousin Red's house on seventy-seventh and Raymond. That was our hang out spot, and we kicked it over there. Her cousin red's boyfriend had just got into an altercation with some cats, 111 Gangsta Crips if I'm not mistaken and was murdered. We went over and smoked with Red and gave her our condolences. There were a lot of murders in the California neighborhoods; they were killing like it wasn't a thing. They were true gang bangers, and if you went on their turf beefing, they were sure to smoke you.

With one day left in California, we ate, shopped, shopped and ate. My mom was having a ball and enjoyed being with Renee and me. It was one of the most relaxing trips that I had in a long time. I wasn't there for business or to meet men I was chilling and relaxing with my mother and my homegirl.

We arrived back in K.C., and there was a murder waiting on me that happened on Sunday night. They found the homeboy Tank from the neighborhood dead. He was my boy, and someone he knew had robbed him and killed him. It was so crazy how all the homies were dying. His funeral would be a day before my birthday party, so we would also have a home going moment of silence for him at the party.

Richie Rich called and asked me to hang out with him the night before the party because he didn't do crowds. I agreed and got dressed. Whenever I hung out with Richie Rich, I always tried to look my best, even though we were just hanging out. He knew I wanted him, but we kept it in the friend zone. We hooked up, went out and had a few drinks talked and laughed. I told him that I had some Cuban cats that had jewelry for sale. He said he wanted to check it, and maybe grab some pieces from them, so we headed over there.

When we arrived, I told him that they had a lot of money, but they had a lot of roaches in the house to watch his back. We were drunk as hell and cracking up. When my boy Ulysses answered the door, the roaches greeted us too. These cats had money, out the ass, and bricks, and had more roaches than a dirty girl in the projects. We went over to the table, and Richie Rich checked out the jewelry. He liked it and ended up spending twenty thousand dollars on two pieces. Ulysses fired up some of his bomb buds, and we smoked and talked for a minute. As we were leaving out of the house, Richie Rich told Ulysses that they needed to bomb the damn house to get rid of all of those roaches. I was high as hell and couldn't help but crack up in Ulysses' face. When we left out, I told Richie that he was crazy telling that man about his roaches like he had known them and they were cool. We laughed like hell.

I was back working on my birthday party. I was going to dinner with people all week; everyone was taking me out for dinner and drinks. I was having a great week, and Saturday was approaching fast it was soon to be going down. Shelter seven was about to make history because I was going to bring the whole city and surrounding states out to this mega event.

Mac came through and smoked all week, he also gave me three hundred dollars' worth of food stamps that he had scored off some fiend, and now I had thirteen hundred dollars' worth of stamps to get more food for the party. We were about to do it super big. Friday was here, and the party was tomorrow. I had J.C. to drive me to Sam's Club because he had a big trunk in his Delta 88. I could get a lot in his car because my little Chrysler convertible couldn't hold anything. We rode out smoking and bumping some old spice; welcome to the ghetto. I was feeling good, and my party was going to be great. It was my birthday, and I was feeling like my name, a Queen!

I got home, Mac, Renee, Tracy, and everyone was over. Renee, Vickie, and Tabby helped me prep the food. I was a cook and my boy Ant would handle the grilling tomorrow. I would season the meat and let it marinate so when tomorrow came I wouldn't have to do anything but have a ball. We smoked and drank on Remy VSOP and XO; we talked a lot of trash for the rest of the evening. Anthony called and wished Angel and I a happy birthday; so, did Jon-Jon, Rashad and everyone else that was locked up in state or federal prison. I had a lot of love in the jail system, and I showed everyone locked up love as well.

Chapter 18

The Birthday Bash

The day finally arrived, and I was ready to party, and so was the crew. We laughed about me inviting all the cats that liked me. I was cool with having them all there because not one of them was my man, just random guys to kill time with when I was bored, and they knew it. I wanted Richie Rich, and he was currently the only one who could get it in the town. He said he wasn't coming to the party because someone told him that my play brother wanted to rob him. He asked me if I knew anything about it and I told him that if he said it, he was just talking, and if he saw him he just might hit him with that heat. He was mad and didn't want to talk to me for a minute, so I backed off.

I went on decorating the shelter for the party it was going digital in a few hours.

It was a beautiful sunny June day. June 8th to be exact, my birthday party had already started, we were kicking it hard. Usually, I would celebrate my birthday with Angel because our birthdays were a day apart. We were not this year; there wouldn't be any children around just the grown and sexy. Shelter number seven was going to make history today. We were ready to party like rock stars. Everyone was showing up; all the D-boys were pulling up in their best whips, all the hot girls came out knowing all the cats with money would be there. I had several bags of bud bagged up and ready to sell, one-hundred-dollar bags or better that's what it was today. It was going to be a day to remember.

Mac had pulled up with his crew and some new cats from Cali that I hadn't met before, they were all some fine brothers, and we were checking them out. Mac introduced us to his friends, and they all pinned the fifties and hundreds on me, the money was coming fast, and I loved every bit of it. The crap game going on was where all the big money cats were. There had to be about ten thousand down on the concrete; Big Ike was running the game. I and his daughter didn't get along because she was messing with Charlie's husband, but I and Big Ike were cool, and he loved crap games. Mac and his boys joined the crap game; someone was going come up on some big money because they were not playing with small bills.

My girls Tracy, Charlie, Vickie, Tabby, and Trecie, were serving the fruit out of the watermelons with their hula dresses on; they also greeted everyone that showed up. They looked so cute everything was perfect I felt just like a Queen, I was the queen, and I had brought the whole city out to Swope Park, well the state, I had cats even show up from St. Louis, my Kansas people also showed up in packs.

After Tracy and J.C. went and grabbed the part for the turntables that D.J. Les needed to play the music it was on. D.J. Les was rocking those turntables, and I was ready to get my party on. I was greeting and welcoming everyone to my birthday luau. Chicks that didn't like me and my crew even showed up, it was the party of the year and if you were not there than you were nobody like I always say if you can't beat them join them.

I had three cats that liked me there so I was feeling like a player and they probably were feeling the same not knowing that I was kicking it with all three of them on the low. I played hard just like the niggas that I dealt with. I was just like them, a female baller/gangster.

Charlie came and penned a few more twenties on me; the money train was awesome! I knew by the end of the day that I would have at least two thousand dollars penned on me and if the night was good maybe three thousand. The twenties, the fifties, and the hundreds were coming real fast. As much liquor as I had people were still bringing fifths of Remy Martin and cases of beer, and we already had two kegs.

The leftover liquor would go home with me for sure. We were going to party non- stop my birthday lasted all month because that's how I celebrated it. I was down the hall chatting with some of my school friends; we were laughing at J.C. and Bug riding on that ugly little moped that J.C. had ridden to the party. Bug was a thick girl, and J.C. was riding her on the back of that little ugly thing he called a moped. I had never seen a bike so ugly I was as high as a kite cracking up at them. They were entertaining everyone. I walked over greeting more people. When suddenly everybody started running and screaming, I ran also. I didn't know why they were running, but when black people see people running, it is usually about to be some bullshit. Next thing I heard was Pow! POW! Pow! POW! I hit the ground next to a car and laid there for a minute; my heart was beating so fast it was all I could hear. I just knew it had to be something that had gone wrong with that crap game because of all that money that they had on the ground. When I finally got up and ran up the hill to see what went down. Vickie was holding him, rubbing his head telling him not to die and telling him everything was going to be alright. J.C. had got shot and was laying there bleeding to death. J.C. was my best friend and Angel's Godfather, and now I was standing here watching him die. Everyone was crying and screaming for help. I was wondering what had just happened so quick; he had just driven past me on that ugly ass moped, now he was on the ground bleeding, fighting for his life. The ambulance finally arrived and rushed him to Research Hospital that was eight minutes away; he was pronounced dead on arrival.

I cried and cried; I knew that it wasn't my fault, but it happened at my party. I thought about how the night before we were at the house kicking it and J.C. went in Angel's room, sat on her bed and watched her for a whole hour while she was asleep. I thought about his son that just had been born and cried, for him. I went to my room and fell on my knees and prayed to God about J.C. and all my problems. Whenever I was going through something, I called on my heavenly Father, and he never failed me.

We went home and watched the video footage that we had shot, up until the shooting, it didn't show the actual shooting, but you could hear the gunshots and people screaming. When I found out what started the shooting I was really pissed. They were going at it about a carjacking that happened two years ago. I couldn't believe niggas could be so petty, but this was K.C., and they robbed and killed over anything, but why at my party? They could have damn sure picked another day, place and time.

Angel was really hurt about J.C. He was her Godfather, and she loved him. She had question after question. Jon-Jon was out of her life and now J.C. The two men she loved the most were gone. I prayed to change my lifestyle for the sake of Angel and Lil' B but every time I tried to the devil stepped in, and I was back to the bad habits. I really couldn't blame the devil; I was on some bullshit. I gave J.C.'s family all the meat that didn't get cooked at the party and apologized to his mother; she loved her oldest son. J.C. was strung out on that sherm like a lot of people in the town, but he was loved, still had money and kept himself up, we had prayed that he would recover from the wicked drug, now it was too late.

Monday morning, we were awakened by a loud boom, boom at the door it was the Kansas City Police with a search warrant for the videotape that we had recorded. I handed it right over because we had weed in the house and didn't need them searching the house, we also didn't have anything to hide on the tape. I handed it over, and they said that they would see me again because I was going to be one of their witnesses. I didn't see anything so why did they want me to be a witness? I had issue after issue. The more money I stacked the more problems I had.

J.C.'s funeral came the following week, and we all paid our respects. It was such a sad, senseless murder, with a stupid cause. The pastor preached about how the younger generation was dying so much sooner than, the older people who just lived long stress-free life. The pastor told all of us young people to stop making excuses because the sun is almost down! He had a nice message, and I listened well. I was a church-going sister, so I listened to any pastor that made sense. On the way to the burial, we were listening to E-40 "*I Practice Looking Hard*," the part was playing, I guess we are living in the last days, cause in the last days the bible speaks of aids plagues, brothas killing brothas, earthquakes, niggas trying to earn stripes is it worth this? I am a sucka if I don't pull yo hoe card nigga. I practice looking hard. He was preaching some real shit just like the Rev. because that's just what was going on and when would it stop? Could it get better or would it just remain the same?

After the funeral, I went home and laid down; the phone was ringing off the hook with all the jail cats calling to see what went wrong. News in the jail spread faster than it did on the street, and they were blowing my line up. I didn't want to talk, so I cut off the phone and laid on my bed in silence.

Mac and Tabby woke me up to some of the best smelling chronic in the world. They knew how to cheer me up. Mac popped a bottle of Cristal and fired a couple of blunts up. He told me to smile like I do because nothing that happened was my fault and don't let anyone tell me different. He also told me that he was going to Texas to be with his wife for a few weeks and that he had a proposition to make with me. I asked him what it was. He said that he had ten pounds of the Chronic left he said that he would sell me five of them for twenty thousand dollars, and sell five of his for sixty-five hundred I said it's a deal. I could sell all ten pounds for seventy-five hundred dollars easy and on the breakdown, make nine to ten thousand on each one. He told me he would drop them off when he was on his way out the city. I knew all I had to do was call J. Bo and he would have one of his little soldiers drive up and grab as many as I wanted to get off. I would give them to him for fifty-five hundred because he knew how the Cali prices went plus he could go out to L.A. and grab his own with no problem, but these were right here in the Midwest right down the street from the Lou. We always helped each other if we had a hook up; he was also moving those things, and I didn't want any parts of that. I loved my bro because he was the man in St. Louis; a straight up boss and showed nothing but love when we arrived.

June flew by fast, and I still was thinking about J.C. wishing that he was sitting next to me talking crazy like he always did. I missed him very much. Angel still was asking questions like, why was J.C. dead. It was sad, and all I could tell her was that everyone had to die. I explained to her that everyone has a day and that one day we all were going to go home, I just hoped we went to heaven. It was time for a vacation; I decided to take Angel to California since we didn't get to have our party together and my party had gone so wrong. I wanted to make up for it. I called Mika, my girl that had been down with me from our younger years. She had shit together and always had money. I called and asked would she like to come along with her daughter and niece? I told her that I was going to take Angel and Vickie's daughter Shug. She responded with of course. By the weekend, we would be on the plane headed to Cali with the kids.

I called Poo to grab Angel and me some clothes and swimsuits. She got right on it. My booster girls were the best. I just hated when they got caught. Poo had been to jail a few times for shoplifting, but just like the rest of the boosters they made bond and went right back to stealing. When I got caught, I was finished. I didn't want to be in the penitentiary for stealing. The boosters in K.C. were true hustlers making really good money, a thousand or two every day was a good come up, and my girls were giving the malls the business.

Poo got Angel and me over fifteen hundred dollars' worth of clothes. She never charged me much because we helped each other and she was living with me at the time. I didn't charge her to live, and she returned the favor with great clothing, nothing cheap. She grabbed me

DKNY and BCBG, and she got Angel Tommy Hilfiger and Guess. We could work with that and be ready for our vacation.

Mac came through before I left and I was happy to see him. He had been going to Texas a lot trying to reconcile with his wife. I prayed that they would get back together, but Mac had to straighten up. I hated to see good women get played by their husband or their boyfriend. We could put our all into loving a man and get used and abused. No matter how good you were to your man, he was still going to cheat. I watched it with my mother and father and history just repeated itself over and over. I hung with a lot of guys, and they all cheated on their women. They would have the best women in the world but would run around screwing the nastiest, sluttiest, little hood rat in the hood. Men could have five women, but if we did it, we were straight up hoes. That's why I got what I could out of these cats because I knew they had other chicks so it did you and I'm going to do me. Women could be so dumb for the man they loved but not me. I knew how it went so I sold them dreams just like they sold dreams to me. I was just like them; fair exchange is no robbery.

We boarded our plane going to L.A. There would be all play and no work. The kids were going to do whatever they wanted. We arrived in L.A.X., grabbed our rental car and started our vacation. After we checked into our room, we immediately went to Roscoe's Chicken and Waffles. Man, I loved my number nine, three wings and a waffle, with a side of cheese eggs. I turned Mika onto it, and she got the same thing, the kids ordered what they wanted while I took pictures of everyone. The kids were looking good, and so was Mika and me, we were sexy chocolate sisters and fly girls at that.

Next stop was to the homie Swany Mack's spot to get chronic and see how he was doing. Swany was my boy and kept the bomb chronic. I could buy a sack and get one free. I really didn't have to buy it, but it was so cheap who cared. I paid fifty dollars for seven grams, back home they were paying two hundred, I looked out for him and his boys when they were down in the town, so whenever I went to Cali, they returned the love. We talked smoked a few Phillies blunts, and I told him that we had to go and take the kids to the beach. I did well because I didn't discuss any business with him this vacation was all about the kids. We arrived at Venice Beach and grabbed a spot. The kids ran straight to the water; I fired up a joint that I had rolled in Zig Zag papers. The bud was so good that it tasted better in papers. I laid out just enjoying the beautiful summer day.

My phone rang with an unavailable call, so I knew that it was someone in jail, I had so many people in jail I didn't know who it would be. I answered, and it was my girl, Marsha. As soon as I accepted the call, she immediately started crying. I asked her what was wrong and why was she crying? She said that she was tired of going through the jail shit and that she just wanted to come home. I told her that she would be home soon and just take it one day at a time. She said, Queen it's something else that I need to tell you. I asked her what it was. She said that she was pregnant and that she was due in August and had no one to take the baby. I thought about what Rashad's mom had told me all those months back, and Marsha lying when I confronted her about the pregnancy rumors. I don't know why she lied, but I was outdone. August was three weeks away, and she was just telling me this.

I asked her who the dad was. She told me King's nephew, Todd. All I could do was shake my head; I asked her what was she going to do? She said that she wanted me to come and get her baby. She was all the way in Bryant, Texas in a federal prison, so I would have to fly to get the baby. Planes were dropping a lot these days. I told Marsha to let me finish my vacation and to call me Tuesday. She said ok, and we hung up.

Marsha was crazy as hell for that stunt that she pulled. She said the baby was Todd's, but she was also sleeping with Mac before she left. I thought about what she said; I told myself that I would pray on it and continued enjoying my vacation. Damn, I just wanted peace.

Mika and I took the kids everywhere, and finally got out and did our own thing. We met a few guys in the lounge while we were having drinks. We chatted they bought a few drinks, we chatted, and we were back to the kids. We ended our trip with taking the kids to Universal Studios and dinner. I had a ball and never worried about what was going on back in K.C. Mika and I balled, it was relaxing. There had been no bad reports, so it was a great weekend in the town also.

Chapter 19

Marsha's Baby

When I got back home, I hooked up with Charlie, Tabby, and Vickie. I told them about the phone call I got from Marsha. I asked them what they thought about me going to get her newborn baby after she was delivered. They said to get the baby and offered to, do their part. I was still pissed that it took Marsha eight months to tell me about the baby. I would have at least had a plan if I had known earlier. I was selling more weed than the law allowed, and now she was hitting me up with a baby?

I spoke to Todd and told him that I spoke to Marsha. I told him that she said the baby she was having was his. He seemed shocked and asked me if I was serious. I told him I was and that I was going to Texas when the child was born to bring her home until Marsha returned. Marsha would be in prison for another year. I explained that I would have to pay the state to pick up the baby. He said that he would help in any way that he could. Todd was pushing weight and didn't have a problem helping people, so I knew he could help, especially if the baby was his.

Richie Rich called and asked me if I wanted to shoot some pool and have a drink. I needed the drink because Marsha had me thinking hard. She was making me change my whole life, but maybe it was a blessing. God knew that I needed to slow down or I would be a victim to the streets. I needed to change my life, and I needed to change it now. So much happened to me that I should have been out of the game, maybe even dead, but I did it for the love of money. It was the root of all evil and with it came problems. Chicks were telling cats that I was bad luck because most of the men I dated died or went to jail. Those situations didn't have a thing to do with me. The silly chicks that talked all the shit didn't have the brains God gave them. If they just sat back and thought for a second, they would realize that all the guys I dealt with were already criminals and drug dealers before I got with them. These were not cats that sold ounces of weed or rocks on the corner. They were heavy hitters, and that comes with consequences.

Richie and I grabbed a drink and a bite to eat. We chatted and laughed about a chick in the restaurant who stared at him the whole time we ate. He was something to look at, I didn't blame her, but he was with me. I couldn't keep my eyes off him either. He was so fine, just like Mace, but even better-looking and smarter. He told me that he was about to expand his business. He said that he was about to open a chain of laundromats. His beauty salon was already jumping. The barbershop side had six chairs as well as the side with the hair stylist. I talked to him about managing the shop because I needed to start working and doing some positive things with my life. Richie didn't think I could settle down and work a 9-5 because I liked fast money too much. He also said that I should get a job because he would never want to see me hurt or doing time for any dumb shit. He said he didn't want his chick with a bag, that he would be the breadwinner and take care of home. I told him I felt the same way about him. I didn't want him to fall victim to the streets. Richie said he didn't do anything illegal and he would be out of this city as soon as he set up the business. He said that he would move to Phoenix, Arizona, or Utah. I told him that one day I was going to leave and go to Florida or Atlanta, Georgia. I loved Atlanta and always wanted to live there. It seemed like black people in Atlanta lived good and didn't hate on one another as they did in Kansas City. Richie had a home in Atlanta already. I never asked Richie for much, probably because we were not having sex, but if I was with him, he gave me money and helped me out just on GP. We were all good, and he was my Boo.

While I was out with Richie, Mac called and said to meet him ASAP at my house. I didn't want to end my date with Richie Rich, but I had to because when Mac said ASAP, we had something working or something was about to go down and didn't anything move but the money. I could look at Richie Rich forever, but money was calling. I told Mac to meet me at Charlie's because that's where I left my car and we could talk over there.

When I got to Charlie's, she was cooking tacos for the children. Charlie had picked up Angel she was playing with Charlie's daughter Tada and her two young sons. Angel and Tada were four months apart and loved each other. Charlie wasn't traveling as much as I did so I had a great babysitter for Angel. Once I got home, Mac finally rolled up with two of his boys smoking super bomb as usual. He got out of the truck and passed it to me. I hit it and choked like hell, almost about to earl. I asked him if this was a new batch. He said yes and that he had to leave and see wifey. They were getting back to where they needed to be. I was happy for him. He told me he had twenty-five pounds of the bomb and I could sell twenty pounds. He said I couldn't buy any for myself but for the price I was selling, it was like it was mine. I could get the bomb weed for three to four thousand dollars from, him. Mac wanted four thousand dollars a pound back for each one he was giving me to sell. I would profit at least forty thousand dollars on that lick, maybe more, but I deducted what I would smoke. I told him I would handle it for him. I also told Mac that I needed anything extra because I was about to fly to Texas and bring Marsha's new baby home. I remembered that Marsha had been sleeping with Mac before she went back to the federal prison. Mac asked who the child's father was and looked very concerned. I told him that it was King's nephew Todd's child, so he was in the clear. He looked confused, so I know he was bare backing Marsha, too. We smoked some more of that heart stopping chronic that he called Mac-a-licious. Mac said he would have one of his boys deliver the bag with the twenty pounds in the morning.

I wanted to get the pack and get it done as soon as I could. I already called my boys in Kansas and sold ten pounds before they touched my hands. I wanted to sell the others one at a time because I wanted seven thousand for each one. I would only owe Mac ten thousand more. I would sell the other ten for fifty-eight hundred a piece, pay Mac his eighty thousand, and walk away with over thirty thousand dollars. I could have made more if I didn't smoke a half ounce a day. Within one week, the weed was gone. I still had a few pounds of my own that I always broke down. I was good and owned my grind.

Richie Rich had been hanging out with Tracy's dude Goldie. They met through Tracy and hit it off pretty good. They were both getting a lot of money distributing chickens and could have helped each other out in some type of way. They were going to Las Vegas for three weeks and were both taking women. Goldie was taking his wife, and I didn't know who Richie was going with, but he told us we could go. Men weren't shit. Richie wanted me to go so when he was tired of his girl he could be in my face. We were not sleeping together so I couldn't be mad at him and his chick. I was a little envious though. I had some extra cash and decided that we would go. Tracy said she would go too. Mike Tyson was fighting Holyfield again, and I never missed the fights, so I was in. I asked Tabby and Charlie if they like to go, and of course, they were in. I spoke with my girl Renee, and she was game too. It didn't matter if I even saw Richie Rich or not while I was in Vegas because I was with my girls and we were going to get on new cats. We stood out like sore thumbs wherever we went. I was single still and ready to catch another baller. I was ready for the weekend getaway. After all, when I came back, I was going to be getting ready to take care of a new baby.

Mac came back into town. He stopped by as soon as he arrived and grabbed his eighty thousand dollars. I was glad because I didn't like holding anyone's money for that long. He trusted me, I never kept money at home. I would keep two or three thousand dollars out so that if I was ever robbed, they could take a couple thousand and go on. I kept all my stacks at Charlie's house hidden and secured very well. I had to protect my money because in this town, as soon as you came upon a good lick, there was someone trying to take it and they didn't have a problem taking your life to get it.

Mac asked if I had spoken to Marsha again. I hadn't because she ran out of minutes. She would call on July 20th when her minutes were restored. I changed the subject and asked how his wife was doing. He filled me in on their time together, and I could tell he was very happy by the smile on his face. I told Mac that she must have put it on him because he was glowing. He smiled and shook his head.

I told Mac that I needed more bud because I was just about out. He said that there was none right now that was worth getting. It was all premature, and they were taxing for it. I knew I had to wait. I was thinking about going to L.A. and getting five pounds from Swan, but I didn't feel like going through all the hassle of getting it home and five pounds wasn't enough. With Mac, I paid for my bud, and he delivered with no hidden fees, and he was bringing twenty-five to fifty pounds, and whatever else they had in that big eighteen-wheeler truck. In L.A., I would have lost. With Mac, I was winning. I played like I only knew about the marijuana that he was selling but I knew he had to be moving birds. The streets talked, and one of my homeboys came and tried to get me to hook him up with Mac. When I told him that Mac only dealt weed, he replied, "Well my boy copped five birds from your boy and always gets bricks from him. I thought, and if you're telling me, I can imagine who else you're telling, it wouldn't be shit for the feds to make him talk." I knew Mac had it going on with the weed and the restaurants, but bricks? I decided not to get involved with that, so I never did hook them up. I didn't trust half of the niggas in K.C. to deal with Mac on five birds. They would have robbed him and me. Mac said that something should be popping up at the beginning of August. I hoped so because I knew I was going to spend a grip in Vegas shopping. I loved to shop. It was my love and my life. Mac said that he was going to head down north to the city and holler at his boys. Keith was my boy, but I didn't like the other cats that Mac was hanging out with. Some cats hung out with people to get things or find out what someone had, and I had a bad vibe. Mac was kicking it with them. He even took the cats to the Super Bowl with him. Dallas was his favorite team. He was a Cali guy who loved the Cowboys. I never talked to the guys when they came around with Mac and I was a people person. Those two were trouble and had scandalous written all over their faces.

I got with Tabby and Charlie, and we had lunch on the Plaza at Houston's. I couldn't get enough of Houston's Hawaiian ribeye. I told them that it was sweet and juicy, just like me. They giggled and said we were something else, and yes, we were. Tabby told us about her new project, an older guy who was giving her a thousand dollars a week. Tabby said the only thing he asked for was for her to blow in his ear and he got off. Charlie and I laughed so hard that I spit my drink out of my mouth. Charlie asked Tabby if the OG had any more friends. We laughed and finished our lunch.

After we finished eating, we walked over, to Halls to see what they had for us to take on our trip to Las Vegas. Halls was a nice upscale store on the plaza that was like a smaller Saks Fifth Avenue. I grabbed a burgundy Prada bag, and Tabby grabbed a black one. Charlie said that she wouldn't dare spend six hundred dollars on a bag, but Tabby and I liked our items, so we purchased them. I went downstairs and bought a bottle of Versace perfume. I loved that fragrance. It smelled great on my body after tearing down the shops; we headed home.

Richie Rich popped up to my house. He usually called, but today he just showed up. I was glad to see, him and had no problem with him showing up unannounced. Richie said that he was at a hotel and it felt like he was being watched. He said he didn't know why but he felt eyes on him. I asked him who he had been dealing with that might have followed him, and he said he only dealt with his small circle of people. I asked him if any of his people got caught up doing anything, and he said that if there was, he wasn't aware of it. I knew Richie had a lot of money, but we never discussed drugs. I knew what was going on, but I stayed quiet. After he had got robbed for that hundred and fifty thousand and wasn't mad, I knew he had to be straight on cash. When he got drunk, he would tell me that he was rich. He would give me a couple thousand dollars just because he was drunk and talking shit. That's how I usually got money out of him. When he was on that Henny, he was generous with his cash. It wasn't much, but I wasn't out to get his money anyway. One day we were at Tracy's house, and she had a couple of our homegirls over that danced. Richie Rich came through with Goldie. Richie wanted one of the girls to strip for him, and I'm sure he would screw her, but he didn't want me around. I didn't know why because we had not slept together and I could have cared less about him getting a lap dance, some head, or whatever he was trying to do. He asked if he could pay me to leave and handed me six crisp hundred-dollar bills.

Goldie and Richie liked watching the strippers get naked and shake their asses. I never wanted to dance nor had the body to do so. I liked getting money without doing anything that had to do with my body. If I wanted to sell pussy, I knew how and did so with no problem. I couldn't run off and sleep with strangers for a few hundred bucks, though, so I only sold it to cats I dealt with. It wasn't my hustle. My girl Jazz danced and got corporate and kingpin drug dealing kind of money for doing it. If I could make the money that Jazz was, it would be a different story. Jazz had white men giving her five and ten-thousand-dollar cashier checks. She was a baller and a dancer and had it straight going on. She kept knots of cash just like my crew and me. We all kept money. We had different hustles but were all getting it in. We had boosters, check writers, drug dealers, strippers, and corporate chicks that equaled a gang of boss ass females doing it better than a lot of the cats that called themselves hustlers. We were more loyal, too. Niggas were telling on each, other and chicks were standing tall. We were the female untouchables. When cats stepped to us, some of them got treated like groupies because that's how most of them. We didn't have love for broke ass niggas. They might have gotten a job from us if we saw potential. They could have sold a few pounds of weed, or even carried some of those heavy ass bags out of the mall.

The cats that we usually dealt with would have never gone for the shit that the crew pulled on those groupie cats. The cats we dealt with had the money, so they tried to tell us what to do. Sometimes I listened, when I was getting what I wanted. Tracy loved Goldie and what he said went. He was married, but he loved Tracy as well. He might have loved a few more women, but that was a man for you. Tracy wouldn't mess around on her man. None of us did. If we had a man, we were down and loyal to him. But I was single and could do whatever I wanted. I had a cat that I could see in several states and get treated like a queen by all of them.

I met a guy in Vegas when I went to one of the Mike Tyson fights. My boy from K.C. hooked me up with him. The cat saw me walking down the walkway and told Milan and his boys that he wanted me. Milan saw that it was me and told the cat that it was his lucky day because I was his homegirl. Milan and I were cool, and he told the cat that he picked a winner. His name was Sal. He was from Queens, New York. I told him that my name was Queen that I would be his queen. We laughed and talked long enough to exchange numbers. He favored Biggie Smalls and was dressed to impress, like a superstar. He smelled great! He wasn't cute at all but looked and smelled like money.

I returned to K.C. We talked for a few weeks then I went to NYC to hang out with him. Sal bought me a plane ticket. He picked me up from the airport in a 1996 600 V12 Mercedes Benz. He was so kind and such a gentleman; He wasn't like the other arrogant cats that I met from New York. They were cocky and rude, but he was cool. He was calm and fly with a gangster look. He had on a solid diamond earring like my brother J. Bo wore and he had on fly Gucci shades and smelled like a million bucks. It turned me on when a man smelled good. His cash made him handsome.

Sal and I went to a spot called City Island and feasted on fried crab legs. The food was great! We talked and got to know each other. Even though we talked for hours every day on the phone, we still had a lot to chat about. After dinner, we checked into a hotel room in Jersey City. It was the loveliest hotel I had ever seen apart from the ones in Vegas. There were a set of steps that lead downstairs, and when Sal took me down, I couldn't believe my eyes. There were a private swimming pool and Jacuzzi in the room. We were already tipsy, so I took off my clothes and jumped straight in the hot tub. Sal joined me, and in the hot tub, we made magic. I broke Sal off so well that I knew the rest of my stay would be smooth sailing. He didn't give the best sex, but I made it work. After the sexual escapade and wonderful evening that we spent together, we woke up, showered, and headed out to shop. Sal had over five thousand dollars in his pocket, and I was trying to spend it all. We went into a jewelry store where I saw a Movado watch that I liked. It had an eighteen-hundred-dollar price tag on it. I couldn't stop looking at it, and Sal purchased the watch without saying another word. I was all smiles and I felt special. We left and went down Fifth Avenue to the Macy's store. I grabbed a couple of Donna Karen outfits and a pair of shoes. Sal spent about another eight hundred dollars. I was truly feeling this man. I returned back to my friends where I was staying after hanging out with him, my girl Sky lived in Jersey in nice townhome. Sal and I spoke for a few more months, but one day when I called, the number was disconnected. I don't know if he went to jail or what happened but we never spoke again. It was good while it lasted, but as the saying goes, "nothing last forever." Sal was my kind of guy. What a life I was living and loving. Every time I went to Vegas I came upon a baller. They would ask me what my occupation was. I never told them that I sold drugs. I told them that I was a chef and I did catering. I didn't lie; I just didn't tell them about my other job. It wasn't their business. I would tell them one day if it came to it. If they were getting money and I knew that I could profit from it, I told them.

Richie Rich called and asked if I was back in town. He said he was around the corner and was going to stop by. When he arrived, he came in and spoke to my mother and daughter Angel. Richie and I took a ride. He called his mom and told her that we were going to stop by. I liked his mom; she was real cool. Richie Rich gave her whatever she wanted. He had a younger sister, too. We hit it off well. I hit it off with anyone I met. I was nice and a people person. I always smiled. After all, I had nothing to frown about. My life was going fine.

Before we got to his mother's house, Richie told me that his best friend whom he had known just about his whole life was acting strange lately. He said that his movements were funny. I told him that I had been seeing him out a lot. There was a nice outdoor mall in Leawood, Kansas on 119th and Roe called Town Center. I went there to shop a lot, and every time I went, I would see him, like he was meeting a chick for lunch or something. We would speak, and I would keep it moving.

I told Richie to always follow his first mind, and he said that he was done giving his best friend Red anything. Richie never discussed giving anyone work with me unless he was tipsy, and it was never about cocaine. This was the first time he was sober and confiding in me. I guess he felt he could trust me, but who could you trust these days? Everyone was scandalous in the town. It was sad that when you had something going on, people always hated on you. What happened to "let's all get money and be happy for one another?" It didn't exist. I asked Richie if he recalled what Red said a few weeks back. We were all sitting around the salon one evening, and everyone was laughing and talking about hoes and snitches around the town when the discussion got deep about who was telling on who. Red said that he would never do twenty years for another nigga, and somebody came out and asked what about five. Red looked at the cat with a smirk that said to me that he would turn on someone if he had to. I just looked at him and shook my head. He had already sold his soul to the alphabet boys in my eyes. Richie Rich missed it, but I watched and listened very carefully to what people said and never forgot anything. I told Richie to be worried because family and friends sometimes was our worst enemies. We got to his mom's house, and when we walked in, his mom and sister screamed, "Happy birthday!" It was Richie's birthday, he hadn't mentioned it. I felt stupid for not knowing, but that's how secretive he was. I guess I was making progress even to be celebrating the day with him and his family. His mom gave him the fluffiest Polo robe and slippers to match. It was wrapped so beautifully, sitting inside a Halls bag. I loved Halls. It was the best store we had apart from Saks Fifth Avenue. Mrs. Rich said she didn't know what to get someone that had everything. Her gift was great! I wished that I would have known. I would have gotten him something nice. I was just glad that I was with him and it was his birthday.

We headed to the Niecy Lounge to have a couple of drinks. Richie didn't party at the clubs much, so Niecy's was perfect. He showed up at the party spots sometimes, but he wouldn't stay long. Tonight was a special occasion, and we partied hard. Charlie, Tabby, Vickie, Tracy, and Ronnie, my cousin Sedalia, came up to the lounge. We drank on Remy Martin VSOP all night and took shots of King Louis XIII.

Goldie stopped in and ordered us more drinks. We had a great time amongst ourselves and the few people that we dealt with. The broads and men hated as usual. We could have been out of town going hard, but tonight it was Kansas City's finest doing it big in our city and giving the money to a black-owned business.

Everyone had gotten drunk and was ready to go home. Tracy, Ronnie, and I stayed with Richie. We headed to North Kansas City to a strip club, and there were a white people than blacks, so all eyes were on us. Ronnie, Tracy, and I came in giggling and dancing. Richie still looked very calm, but he was drunk just like we were. I checked him out for a minute, thinking tonight would be the night, but I didn't want to be drunk the first time we had sex. That would mean we did it all for the wrong reasons, and he would have been thrown upon. He was so fine. His puppy dog eyes were to die for and his caramel skin made me want to taste him. His lips were luscious, his hair stayed lined up, and he stayed fly in the latest Polo. Whenever the time came, he would most definitely get my all.

I snapped out of my lustful daydream when Richie handed me a shot. I looked at him seductively, smiled, and took my drink. I told him that I was just thinking and he told me to hold the thought. We downed a whole tray of pork ass Jell-O shots that the waitress brought over to our table, and I think that's how I got sick. We were all drunk as hell. Richie told one of the black dancers to come and dance for him. I guess since he was black, she didn't think that he would tip well because cats in Kansas City were just being turned on to the strip club nightlife. Atlanta was known across the country for its strip clubs. The dancers there got paid. Magic City and the Gentlemen's club in the A was the shit. In the Kansas City strip clubs, the girls didn't even get naked, nor did the black men tip well.

Unfortunately, the dancer didn't know who she was dealing with tonight. She walked away and started dancing for the white guys who were throwing her ones. She may as well have been getting quarters thrown at her. A thin white girl with a super flat ass that really couldn't dance came over and started dancing for Richie. He didn't pay her much attention, but after one song Richie dropped five hundred singles in front of the frail stripper. Her eyes got big, she started shaking the little ass that she had even harder, and Rich was showing the black chick what she could have had. The black chick looked real dumb watching while she got sprinkled with singles, and the chick dancing for him got five hundred in one wop.

We left club, Ronnie was throwing up all over, and we were all drunk as hell. I didn't know how we were going to make it all the way to Martin City from North Kansas City. Richie Rich was drunk as hell driving doing a hundred miles an hour. We were in a sports car, but he was going way too fast, doing way too much. I was so drunk I just closed my eyes and went to sleep. When I woke up, I was home, and still in one piece. Thank God. I was sick for the next few days, but it was well worth it because I got a chance to kick it with my dream boy for his birthday.

The week had gone by fast, and I decided to take Angel and Charlie's kids swimming. I loved the kids and did as much as I could with them when I wasn't on the go. Little B was a pre-teen and started coming around too. Things were falling into place. I was glad that he could see I wasn't the monster that his dad portrayed me to be. I loved my kids and told them every day. I sold drugs, but I took care of my home and tried to keep my kids out of harm's way. I always justified what I was doing although I knew it wasn't right.

When we got home from the pool, Mac was pulling up. He never called, and would never have to. He was welcome whenever. Mac pulled out his sack and started rolling blunts. I ran upstairs, showered, and was ready to get my head right. Mac said he found some bud he liked that was coming on Monday, but it was only twenty pounds. He said that he could sell me five. I didn't care if it was only one pound, I needed it. I knew I would have to break them all down and not sell any weight. I couldn't wait until his plug got back right. We had been going strong for years, and now the drought was tearing my pockets up. I didn't like when the drought came because I found myself dipping into my stashed cash.

Monday would be perfect because we were going to Las Vegas on Friday. I wouldn't have to go into the stash now. I would only have to put the money that I took out to get the five pounds and the extras that I made off it. I sold a couple of pounds before the weekend even came. I broke the rest down; I left a half a pound with my play daughter Coco and was ready for Vegas.

Tabby, Charlie, Renee, Tracy, and I all rode together to the airport. I left my truck there. I had a 2006 Toyota Four Runner that had plenty of room. We drove that truck everywhere. I put a whole lot of freeway miles on it. Richie's plane was leaving later that day, so I would get up with him when he arrived in Vegas. I was ready to play with my girls.

As soon as we stepped off the plane and had gone to baggage claim, I was getting numbers. They were choosing already. Vegas and Atlanta airports were the shit. I always got numbers while I was there. Maybe I would make a love connection in one of them.

This was the first time we went to Vegas without staying in a hotel. Our homegirl Shonda had moved there from K.C., and we all stayed at her spot in North Vegas. She had a nice cozy spot, and we could smoke weed without worrying about putting a towel up to the door and being thrown out. We unpacked, got dressed, and headed to the strip. There would be no sleeping this weekend. I loved the strip. It was beautiful, anything was better than being in the town. Every time we went there, there was another hotel being built.

I went straight to a crap table when we walked into Caesar's Palace. Renee and Charlie played slots, Tracy and Tabby peeped the scene...Mike Tyson knew how to make Vegas pop. After I lost a couple of hundred dollars fast, I headed to the Gucci store. I bought a thousand-dollar pair of black boots, and Tracy bought a bag. We balled out anytime we came to Vegas. After shopping, I started checking out cats with Tabby and Tracy. We only had seven grams of weed left with us, and I knew that it would be gone by morning. I told Tabby that we had to find a cat that had some bomb. I told her to start looking for Cali cats because they were out there getting paid on that chronic.

We all knew how to spot Cali boys. They walked slew foot, always had their flannel shirts buttoned all the way to the top of their necks, chucks, and dickies on, and their chest out.

I spotted a cat, and he was most definitely from L.A. and might have been a gang banger. He had his Levis on with his Rolex chain swinging. He was six-foot-six. His hair was pretty and long platted up, with his gangster chucks on. As soon as he hit the corner our eyes met. My cousin Ronnie taught me how to work my eyes when I needed to get what I wanted, and most of the time, it worked. I pulled his ass right over like I was a magnet. He said that his name was Big Ant from Main Street Crip. He told us we could get some bomb at the Bally Hotel where he was staying. He told us to ride over there with him, and he'd give me a couple of stories. Only two of us could go because he was in his tow truck, so Tabby and I went. We told the other girls that we would be back and to wait on us. He seemed cool to roll with, so we didn't hesitate. We got to Big Ant's tow truck; It was fresh as hell, one of the hardest that I had seen for a tow truck. He said he came to Vegas on fight weekends and racked up on cash, and if someone from L.A.'s car messed up he could tow it back to L.A. He had a good thing working with his eagle claw, flatbed truck.

When we got to Big Ant's room, you could smell the weed as soon as his door opened. He said he didn't smoke, just now and then. He pulled out a brown bag full of weed. It was about five ounces. I could eyeball purple; I didn't need a scale. He pulled out his Zig Zag papers and rolled Tabby and me the fattest joint ever. It was dang near bigger than a blunt. He laughed at us choking when we fired up. The bud was so fire. He rolled us a joint for the road, and we headed back to Caesar's.

When we got back to Caesar's Palace, Richie Rich and Goldie had popped up. If he was with a chick, I didn't want to see her. I was hating for real and was crushed. We weren't together but he damn sure acted like we were. Why did he want me to come to Vegas anyway? So his ass wouldn't be bored with his square ass date.

I told old boy with the Cush thanks and that I would be calling him soon.

Once back at the casino, Goldie giggled and said, "I see you, Queen, you be making moves baby." I smirked and walked over to Renee and Tracy. I told them what the big homie had given me. The joint was so big that I could break it down and make two blunts. I was high and feeling fly. We left Caesar's and went to a bar at the MGM Grand. It was packed like hell. The fight would be there the following night, so the hotel was mad packed already. There were fine men everywhere. The ladies were also fly as hell. You had to have your game right during fight weekend, and we were ready. The cats were checking us out. Richie Rich had on a Rolex watch. The lady at the jewelry store in Caesar's told him that he had one of the best-looking Rolexes that she had seen all week. His arrogant ass liked the compliment and was walking around cocky. He was rich so he could do that. I liked rings, not watches, and I had on the ring that King had given me for Christmas. It was a three and a half karat with a sixteen-thousand-dollar price tag. It shined like the sun. We were Kansas City's finest, putting K.C. on the map.

We hung out all night. Charlie, Tracy, and Renee took it in at 5 a.m. Tabby and I saw our boy D from the Lou. He was with a few cats and some chicks. We rode around in a limo with them. We smoked and popped a couple of bottles of Cristal. By eight, I was wiped out. They dropped us off at the house.

At ten, my phone was ringing I sounded like a monster with my raspy voice, but answered. It was Richie Rich telling me to get up and cook some breakfast for him and Goldie. He was crazy as hell. With all the restaurants around the strip, why would he call me so early? He had several in his hotel and room service as well but wanted me to cook. I hadn't even gotten two hours of sleep, but I was right back at it again. We were in Vegas and hell with the way I felt; I could sleep when I died.

We cooked a big breakfast for Goldie and Richie. They were right back over here messing with us while the women they came with were who knows where. It was cool until I asked Richie for a lousy thousand dollars. I didn't need it, but I asked because I knew that he was buying his broad something and it would be more than a thousand dollars if she knew who she was dealing with. Now I was pissed because he hadn't delivered it. He ate and left. I got dressed, left, and did what I did best, mingle. I didn't have anything else to say to Richie, and if he wasn't going to give me what I wanted, he could kiss my ass.

After the fight, we went next door to the MGM to a party that Shaquille O'Neal was throwing. Tabby and I walked straight in as usual, just like we were celebrities, without paying a dime. We walked right in behind Shaq like we were his guests. I hated paying two and three hundred dollars to get into clubs just because celebrities were in the building. They were people with money just like us. In my mind, my girls and I were celebrities too.

Once we got inside of the club, Tracy and I made our way through crowd, standing out like we always did. All eyes were on us. We weren't celebrities, but you couldn't tell. I immediately locked eyes with a cat that I learned was from Baltimore. They were popping bottles of Cristal like it was going out of style. He motioned for me to come over and I told my girls we were going to the VIP because if I went, my girls went too. We had a ball with the Baltimore and DC cats. I hadn't drunk so much champagne in all my life. We popped bottles of Cristal with Mac but nothing like we were doing this night. I exchanged numbers with a guy named Avon, and I was on to the next one. I might have had ten numbers when I left Vegas, but when it narrowed down, I only had one or two that I kept in touch with.

We partied until we couldn't party anymore. We had a ball like we did all the time.

The next day, it was time to get back to K.C. back to reality as we always said. I didn't see Richie again in Vegas, but I knew that he would be popping up at my townhouse as nothing happened. Since he had been around, I didn't holler at other cats, especially in the town. He wasn't my man, nor had I slept with him, but I guess that's the type of hold he had over me and I showed him respect because he was a super boss to me and not a suck. I had money and didn't need a man. I needed them when I wanted them, and that wasn't often until I wanted sex. I was too busy moving around to be worried about a man, who he was cheating on me with, or what he was doing. I had enough to worry about with Richie and how he dodged me in Vegas and was still on bullshit. I was hot with him because he should have given me the little cash that I asked for. I finally let go of the grudge when I realized that I was being petty and selfish. I wanted the money because I knew he was with someone else, and felt it would make me feel better to say I got something from him. It wasn't about money. It was about my pride. He didn't owe me a dime. Richie was going to be my friend regardless of the dumb issue.

Chapter 20

Reunited with Little B

It was a beautiful August day. We were getting dressed for church and Angel was brushing her beautiful hair. She had grown up so much. I was proud of her. She was almost a teenager. My son Little B moved back, and we were one happy family. We would go to church and then eat at Tabby's. Tabby and her sister Vickie could cook like me, they didn't play.

Tabby and I always tried to make it to church when we were in town or not hungover from the night before.

We got to church, and the Bishop spoke of the book from Corinthians.

"We walk by faith, not by sight" (II Corinthians 5:7).

I knew I needed to get right with God. I prayed and cried and asked God for forgiveness. I knew I did devilish things but I loved the Lord, and I knew He loved me. When people told me, I was going to hell for something that I'd done; I told them that their sin was no less than mine so I would see them burning next to me. Despite all my faults, God always brought me through. I knew that He was right by my side. We received prayer and gave a generous tithe and offering, and then we were off to Tabby's.

Tabby cooked up a feast: baked chicken, fried chicken, beef ribs, macaroni and cheese, greens, cornbread, and much more. Mac stopped by and fired up. He lit up a couple of blunts, and I thought about how I left the church and prayed to change my life. But the devil was busy, and he kept taking me the way that I wasn't supposed to go. I can't keep blaming it on the devil, he can't get all that credit, but I just wasn't ready to change. Mac said to quit daydreaming and hit the weed. I snapped out of my thoughts and started puffing. I told Mac that in the next two weeks, I would come home with Marsha's baby.

We joked about it being his because we knew he had been with Marsha and they were bare backing. He looked crazy and confused when we brought it up and didn't say a word. We ate dinner and relaxed with the family and whoever else popped up for the rest of the day.

Chapter 21

Bundle of Joy: A Child is born

I was watching America's Most Wanted when the phone rang. It was
Marsha calling to say that she was having contractions and that she
would call me when she knew what was going on. I told her that I was
praying for a safe and blessed delivery. After we hung up, the phone
rang again, but this time it was Richie. We hadn't spoken since we left
Vegas. He must have realized that I wasn't going to call him at all. I
answered the phone, and he joked around as soon as I said hello. I
knew that he would act as nothing happened. It wasn't a big deal, but I
was still acting shady with him. He told me he was going to stop by. I
hesitated as I considered telling him not to, but gave in. I wanted to see
him. I missed looking at him. He made me smile for no reason and
always made my day. If you didn't know Richie, you would have
thought he was the meanest, most arrogant person in the world,
because he didn't talk to anyone that he wasn't friends with. If you did
know him, you knew that he was really silly and fun.

I let Richie inside. Usually, I would have fixed my hair in an attempt
to look my best for him, but tonight I didn't care how he saw me. I
looked a mess and kept my lip poked out, pouting. Richie asked if I
was still mad about Vegas. I turned my head and kept watching
television. Richie started tickling me and telling me to get over it. I
was mad, but I couldn't help but laugh, and besides, his touch was
turning me on. I told him to stop, but I was enjoying every moment of
it. By the time he stopped, he was on top of me. I was breathing hard,
looking into his sexy eyes. Suddenly, we were getting naked, and there
we were, finally making mad love to each other. I let him fuck me any
way he wanted, and I sucked on him like he was my own, special
lollipop. I don't know what it was for him, but for me it was
passionate. I felt ecstatic and alive. We sweated and fucked for hours; I

knew I liked him way too much because I never once asked him where his condom was and I was a condom advocate. Tonight, it was raw and uncut.

I wanted to feel every piece of his love up inside of me. I waited for almost an entire year, just for a couple of hours of pure passion, but it was well worth the wait. I had finally made love to my dream boy. But I wondered if the crush would be over, or if the feelings would change as they did with other guys. I decided I didn't need to worry about that for the moment. I was on cloud nine and wasn't even high on weed. I was high on Richie Rich. I lay in bed up under him all night, enjoying the dream that was now a reality.

Bright and early Monday morning, Marsha called to let me know that her daughter was here. She was born the night before. Marsha was going back to prison on Tuesday. She had two days to be with her precious child. I felt bad for her. Who would want to depart and leave their newborn child and not see them again for a year? It hurt me because I knew it hurt Marsha. I told her that I would have to make reservations to fly and get baby Catalina. Two planes had crashed a few weeks before, and now I had to take two different flights to get my new bundle of joy. After I purchased my airline ticket, I called the state worker and asked what I would have to do. She said that I would have to bring six hundred and fifty-nine dollars for the two-day care that the state had provided after baby. Catalina was released from the hospital and I was going to get to Texas on Thursday evening and was paying seven hundred dollars for three days of care. I shook my head and got ready for my trip. All the weed I sold and all the partying that I did…something was going to have to change with the new baby around.

As I boarded the first plane, I prayed for a safe landing in Dallas, Texas. Everything went smoothly, and the next plane that I boarded that was landing in Austin, Texas was just as smooth. Marsha was in the federal prison camp in Bryant, Texas, but the state care agency met me at the Austin Airport. I was picking up the baby and turning right back around. Four flights in one day. I was bound to be jetlagged. I knew the white lady immediately because she was holding a small black baby. We shook hands, I gave her the seven hundred dollars that I got from Todd, I signed consent papers, and the baby was mine, just that simple.

As I boarded my plane back to Kansas City with a five-day-old baby, I prayed that we would be safe and that everything would go well with our transition. She was so precious and didn't cry on our trip home. I knew that once I got home things would have to change. Not just for the baby, but for Angel and Little B also. I didn't want people telling my kids that I was a drug dealer. They were about to be teenagers, and I needed a real occupation. I was going to start looking for a real job as soon as I got home.

Baby Catalina and I arrived back in the city safe and sound. When I got home, Tabby, Vickie, and Charlie stopped by. They were glad to see the baby. Charlie hugged and kissed her, loving on her as an aunty would do. She told the baby that she had been through a lot, but now she was home with her family. She was our gangster baby born in the penitentiary. Now she was ours, and we were going to give her the world. Marsha called to see if we made it back. I told her we did and ensured her that I would take good care of her baby.

Richie Rich stopped by to see the new bundle of joy. He told me that I was a true friend and that God would bless me for the good deed. He told me that once I was settled, we would hang out. Now that we made love, we were chilling at the house instead of hanging at the bar. I enjoyed his company and cooking for him, and I was still attracted to him, just like the first time I laid eyes on him.

I took the baby to see Todd and his family. King had a family that didn't care what came out of their mouths. They were very outspoken. When we arrived at their auntie's house, Todd showed her Catalina.

Aunt Jane looked at her for a few minutes, then came straight out and said, "Todd, that ain't yo damn baby! I know what your kids look like and she doesn't look like nan one." I couldn't do anything but put my head down and shake it. She favored Todd a little, but she looked like Marsha. Vickie said that she looked just like Mac, so now there was a problem. Shit, I didn't know what to think now. Who was Catalina's daddy?

Mac heard that Catalina looked like him. He told me that he was going to come and see what everyone was talking about. I told him to come through, and look her over. She was so precious and now her dad Todd was saying that she might not be his because of what Aunt Jane said.

When Mac showed up, I went out to the truck and smoked a blunt with him. He asked if the baby looked like him, and I told him that she looked like her mom. I told him about the visit to Todd's and how he was unsure about being her father. I asked him if he ready to see her, and when we finished the blunt, we entered the house. When we got inside, Angel was feeding Catalina. I took her and tried to give her to Mac. He said that she was too small and that he didn't want to hold her. He looked her up and down, but all he could do was shake his head and say he didn't know. I told him that the best thing to do was to take a blood test. Mac already had two kids with his wife, and I didn't think he was ready for more. He must have been ready for something because evidently, he hadn't used a condom and when you don't use condoms, you can either come out with a disease or a baby! Mac told me that he wanted a blood test, and was willing to pay for his and Todd's. He wanted to know whose baby Catalina was as soon as he could. I told him that I would see when they could arrange a test. Mac was the true definition of a real man.

I had been in the house for weeks; the only time I went out was to sell a few pounds of weed I got from Richie. I finally found a job at St. Joseph Hospital and tried to get my life on track. Tabby worked at some cleaners. It was like she was the owner. Before I went to work, I dropped Catalina off with Tabby, and she kept her right there in the cleaners. Catalina had lots of love. All the boosters dressed her, and all the girls in the crew watched her. She was truly our baby, the whole clicks.

I was drained from working and getting up with the new baby. Saturday morning, I got up went to the spa. I got a body massage, pedicure, and manicure. I called Richie Rich and told him that I wanted to get out of the house. I had been taking care of the kids and chilling. Later that evening when he picked me up, we went to Jack Stack Barbeque in Martin City, around the corner from my house. We ended up at a hotel. If I wasn't mistaken, I thought he was making D boy moves. He kept talking to someone and leaving the room. He was very uptight and somewhat nervous. After about an hour, he stopped coming in and out and was calm and ready to chill out. We had a drink, talked some, he even took a pull off my blunt once, which is when I knew whatever he had going on had been taken care of. Sex was next on the menu. I gave him the business. Well, we gave it to each other. The sex was better this time. I was comfortable with him. I opened up. After hours of good love-making, we lay in the bed and talked. Richie told me that he was moving real soon. He said he needed to start another business in another state. He never talked about the drug dealing that he had going on, but I knew. I wanted to tell him that he should go before someone started talking and the feds got in his mix, but he already said that he didn't have those types of problems because he wasn't doing it like that. I laid there listening to the great plans that he had for the future. He had a bright future ahead of him if he could get out of Killa City without being murdered or going to jail. I wished that I could spend my life with him because, from the sound of things, he was about to do it real big.

I went down to King's spot and asked him if he could call Todd so I could speak with him in person. When King called, they came with no hesitation, and I didn't like to wait. I had pulled, but King was the godfather of Kansas City. When he said move, they moved. King did anything for me. I was just like his little sister. I loved my real brother Greg, but King, Mac, Scooter, and J. Bo were my balling/player/gangster partners. They all had that paper, and whatever I wanted, one of them was going to make sure I had it. I always said it didn't take blood to make someone your family. They were just as much my family as the blood ones were.

While I sat at King's and waited on Todd, I drank a Corona with lime. King rolled a joint. King smoked with licorice papers and mainly smoked fat joints with nothing but the best weed. He didn't even want to look at dirty weed. None of us did. If it had seeds, they were out of pocket for even trying to pass it to us. King's spot was the gambling spot on 31st and Benton. Niggas would argue and fight sometimes in there, but we still popped up and hung out. We were used to the shit and knew that we could have lost our lives, but we loved King and his boys. The inner-city Player Macs. Their crew was the male version of mine. They did what they had to do to get what they wanted. Their crews of gangsters consisted of bank robbers, killers, and bossy drug dealers. The hell with hitting small licks, they were treacherous, hitting jewelry stores and other licks worth hitting.

When Todd arrived, we sat down, and I told him that I had spoken with Mac. I explained that Mac wanted to know who the father of the baby was. I told him that Mac was willing to pay for both blood tests and that I would arrange the appointment for them to go. Todd said that he was down and that he would be ready once the arrangements were made. I was glad that they had agreed to do the right thing for Catalina's sake. I had to tell Marsha next time she called.

Marsha called the following weekend, and I told her what was going on with Mac and Todd. They would be taking the blood tests in two months. She said that she didn't care, but she knew that Todd was the dad. I told her about his Aunt Jane saying that Catalina wasn't his. She was pissed and said that she didn't know what the hell she was talking about. She said to give them what they wanted.

Mac would come over but wouldn't get close to Catalina. Todd hadn't seen her since the day we went to his aunt's. They were just waiting for the time to test.

Mac got a shipment in. I was working at the hospital, but my cash stash had gotten low, it was crazy how fast money went. I tried to stop selling weed, but I didn't like being broke or depending on anyone. It was calling my name. I went to my stash, grabbed twenty-two thousand and got me five pounds of Northern Lights. Mac told me that after this batch, I could grab ten pounds. He went back to the bay area. He also said that I could get them for thirty-five hundred dollars apiece. I couldn't wait. I thanked him and told him I loved him very much. I liked the fact that I never had to give up money until I had what I wanted in my hand. That made everything even better.

I finally got a day to hang out with the girls. We drank up a fifth of Remy Martin and went to the Epicurean Lounge on Troost Ave. We danced to Tupac's song, *America's Most Wanted*. "ain't nothing but a gangster party." All eyes were on us. The chicks were watching their men like hawks, but if we wanted their men, chances were that one of us could holler at him and succeed. I didn't want a cat from the town anyway. I was cool with most of the cats that I might have tried to date, but the rest were corny and the country as hell, so that's how it would stay. I promised myself that after Jon-Jon, I would never fight over a man again and I stuck to that. Men weren't shit to me, just dogs in my eyes. I thought I loved a few, but I knew when things weren't right to let go because it wasn't meant to be. I messed with all the wrong kind of men. Drug dealers, players, killers, you name it. If they thought they knew how to beat the system, they more than likely went to jail. I couldn't shake no-good men. I guess I wasn't trying to. Now I loved only God and my family. It felt good loving me and being stress-free. Being with a man was stressful and time consuming because I was looking for love in all the wrong places. With men, you would be the baby's momma or the wife that got everything you wanted except his unconditional love. He'd treat you just as bad as the girlfriend, or you were the side chick or the mistress. Fuck all the titles. I was doing me. Married to the game.

The girls and I drank and drank. We were all feeling good. We headed out to smoke some good. Smoking was my man. I had to smoke weed when I drank heavy; It balanced everything out. While we were smoking, Tracy said that she forgot to tell us she had seen the fat, fly cat from Texas the other night at the club. She said he asked about me. I asked her which cat she was talking about because we had met so many men throughout the years. She responded that it was the one from Texas that was talking to Jazz in Cancun. That nigga was arrogant and acting funny. Why was he asking me for? We hardly said anything to each other in Cancun. He was my type, but I wasn't trying to get at him because he and Jazz were shooting the shit and had chosen up. I would have never stepped on Jazz's toes like that. Jazz was close enough to me that I would never screw anybody that she was talking to. Tracy said that he'd be in and out of the city for a while so we should hook up with him. I was game, and I wanted to know what he wanted with me anyway, probably trying to get off some work, and I didn't mess with cocaine at all.

Chapter 22

Gone but Not Forgotten

The month had gone by so fast. Catalina was getting big. She was already in three to six months' clothes and was moving around. I had been staying home a lot. Mac hadn't come through with any chronic in three weeks, so I was dry. It gave me time to get home from work and play with the girls and think about what I was going to do with my life. There were days where I would just fall on my knees and pray and tell God to deliver me from this lifestyle. I was deeper in the game than I ever knew, my thoughts were fucked up. Shit, I was fucked up. It was easy choosing my lifestyle but so hard to get out.

Richie Rich stopped by while I was hung around the house and looked a mess with my thinking cap on. He asked me what was on my mind. I usually didn't talk to him about my business or problems. We just chilled. He never got in my mix, and I never got into his business either. I just knew that he had a lot of money. I told him that I was tired of the lifestyle and all the drama that came with it. He said, "You know how it is, Queen, more money, more problems." I told him that I didn't like working in the hospital, but I needed to do something different. He joked and asked what I was going to do about him. I looked at him and told him we would be friends for life. He smiled with that sexy dimple that gave me chills. I liked him, but it was never a boyfriend/girlfriend thing, and I knew that it would never be more.

I told Richie Rich that my brother was unable to make a connection and that I needed to make some cash. I had spent a lot of money since I was working and not selling weed, and I needed a come-up. I asked Richie Rich if he knew where I could get some cool buds. He said that he'd talk to his people and see what they could do, but that it wasn't the stuff that I was used to. I thanked him, knowing that he was his people.

The babies and I enjoyed the rest of our evening eating pizza and watching movies.

The weekend was great, but it was back to work at the hospital. The job was easy. I was a PSA (Patient Service Administrator). I didn't clean shit or anything of that nature. I just did a little filing and assisted nurses, but I was bored. Eleven dollars an hour wasn't good for me because I was used to hundreds. It was messing with my schedule, and I needed to make moves. I made it through the day.

When I looked at my phone, I realized I had a missed call from Richie Rich. I called him back, and he made jokes as soon as he picked up. I adored his sense of humor.

He asked when I would be home and I told him after I picked up Catalina from Tabby. When I arrived home, I changed clothes. Richie Rich showed up shortly after I got there. He came in with a large trash bag. When I opened it up, there were ten pounds of marijuana in it. I asked him what it was for and he said, "You said you were dry, so I brought you what you needed." I was all smiles. We never talked about business, and now he was bringing me weed. It wasn't chronic, but it was pretty good bud from Arizona that we called K Town. This could be sold for eight hundred to one thousand dollars per pound or more. He told me to give him seven thousand dollars back once I sold it. That would be a cool come up for me. I could go to Kansas and get eleven-hundred-fifty dollars for each one with no problem. I was down with that, and I knew that I would profit well because I didn't smoke K Town unless there was no chronic around. chronic was everywhere. I was getting low since Mac had not been back from the bay area.

After two days, the K Town was gone. I was ready to give Richie Rich his money and get more from him. I called and called, but he didn't pick up. I knew that he would call me because I had his cash. I got dressed and headed to the city. When I arrived at the cleaners, Tabby was sitting outside smoking, and Tracy was pulling up. She got out of her car and said that she had bad news. We asked her what was wrong and she said that she had talked to Goldie and he said the feds had snatched Richie Rich up. When I asked her if I was serious, she told me to get the newspaper.

When I got the paper, the headline was Richie Robinson. It said that they had been watching him for years. It said that they had started watching him way back before the Oklahoma City bombing. When they couldn't get anything from him because he moved so smooth, they left and went to handle Timothy McVeigh, the Oklahoma City bomber. After two years, they resumed surveillance and were on his tail again. I read they had found six hundred thousand dollars and several kilos of cocaine in a storage unit that belonged to him. They also had a cooperating witness. I couldn't believe what I was reading. Why was this happening to me? Shit to him. I had his money, and I held onto it to see if he would call or have someone reach out to me. I wondered who was snitching on him. He didn't let a lot of people in his circle, so who was the rat?

Richie was shipped to Leavenworth, Kansas with no bond and was labeled as a flight risk. He wasn't getting out. I wished I could hug him, or even talk to him.

The weeks were flying by. I was depressed about Richie. I quit my job because I couldn't stop thinking about him and I couldn't focus on my job. He was my homie, my lover, but most of all, he was my friend. He had a court date coming up, and I was going to be there for him.

Mac came through. I told him what happened to Richie. I told him to be careful because niggas were snitching. Mac said that because he only dealt weed, they wouldn't be looking for me. I just told him that I heard the same song from Rich. Mac knew he was moving bricks, and so did I, but I still warned him. He told me that he was ready for the blood test to be over so they could see whose child Catalina was. I told him that in two weeks they would be tested and it would all be over.

Mac said that he was leaving for a couple of weeks and that he would be back before the blood test was to take place. He was happy. He was going home to southern California and then to the bay area to score some chronic. After that, he was going to Oklahoma to bring his wife home. I was happy for my brother. His wife was finally coming back. He said that if Catalina were his, he would tell her because he didn't want to fuck up again. He wanted to treat his wife like the queen she was because she deserved it. I said that all women deserved the best, but men were dogs and they just couldn't help themselves.

It was one of the worst weekends that I'd had in a long time. Richie Rich was gone, and Mac's bald head butt was out of town and wouldn't return for another week. I was used to seeing at least one of them every day, and I was missing both.

Tracy called and said that the cat from Texas called again. She told him that we would hook up with him on Sunday and that I should cook. I told her I would and to bring him through. She said, "Oh, and by the way, his name is Lex."

Saturday was slow and hot as hell. Angel and I took Catalina to Chuck E. Cheese. Even if I weren't happy, at least the kids would be.

I went to church on Sunday morning. I prayed for Richie, Mac, J. Bo, King, my family, and all the friends that lost loved ones to death or prison, and most of all me. I cried out to God and begged him to change my life because I was going down the wrong path. I even went up in the prayer line to get prayer. I needed the Lord, and I needed Him now. I loved the Lord and repented my sins all the time. I wasn't perfect, but God knew my heart was genuine with Him.

After service, I went home and finished cooking dinner before the company came. Tracy finally showed up with Lex. He was looking good just like he was in Cancun. He had on iceberg jeans with Gucci sneakers and the belt to match. He had on diamond Cartier shades looking like a big rich nigga. I liked what I saw. I asked him what he was doing in sorry ass K.C. He said he was trying to start a business and that he would be in and out for a minute. I was about to ask him why he was asking for me and not Jazz but I let it go. We had pot roast, potatoes, fried chicken, yams, green beans, and cornbread. We had a feast. Lex said that it was good, but I needed to try some of his cooking. He was just my type. After we ate, Tracy said she was going to take Lex home. We exchanged numbers, said our goodbyes, and they were out. I had a good Sunday and the weekend turned out just fine.

The new week started, and I was glad Mac would be back on Friday with the chronic. In one week, Catalina would be getting her blood test, and Mac and Todd would know whose child she was. I called Lex and thanked him for coming by. He said we would do it again when I was free. I told him that I was free and whenever he wanted to hang out we could. Yeah, I was flirting. He was already mine.

On Tuesday Vickie and I went to court to see what was going on with Richie. I hated the federal courthouse; It was quiet and cold. It was worse than a funeral home or a library. You could hear a pin drop. The feds had also snatched up Richie's mother and had her in custody. It turned out that Richie's best friend Red had been snitching on him and his mom. I knew Red wasn't right. When I used to see him at the mall out on 119th and Rowe, I could smell a rat. I knew that he was up to something. Shit, he was up to no good. He was meeting federal agents and setting Richie up the whole time. In court, the prosecutor said the only way that they could get to Richie was through his best friend Red. He didn't use mules to get his drugs. They said that if the main connect didn't bring his drugs, he didn't want them. Red had sold his soul to the devil and did him in. Over fifty kilos of cocaine were entered into evidence from Red. The wiretaps were unbelievable. Red set Richie and his mom up tough. The feds also confiscated twelve Rolex watches, a few houses, ten cars, and titles from Richie. I was astounded. Richie had all kind of shit. A millionaire just like he said and the feds took it all. Vickie was sitting there saying things like, "Damn, he had it going on." He did, but what goes up must come down.

Wednesday came, and I was getting excited. I was totally out of bud and needed my pack. I couldn't wait for Friday to get here but now the week was moving slow, and I had to wait. I hung out with my girls and smoked. They always made the day better when things weren't going well. We had each other's backs and were always there for each other when something went wrong in our lives. We went out to dinner at Ray's Seafood and got drunk and full. Lex called, but I didn't answer because I was thinking about Richie and staying focused on making my money. I didn't want to be caught up with a man. I was focused on myself.

Thursday was a good day, and it was going down. I started reading a book called *If Tomorrow Comes* by Sidney Sheldon. It was so good that I finished it by the end of the day. I had a passion for reading. It made the day go by faster.

Friday finally came, and I went down to Russie's Salon on 18th and Brooklyn. It was located on top of Wings and Things Restaurant. I knew that I was going to be on the move all weekend and I was going to be fly doing my deliveries. Russie's was packed, but as usual, I walked in and jumped right into the chair. I was in and out. I didn't have time to sit around the salon all day and mess with Russie because he would have chicks waiting for hours, but not me. After my hair was done, I went downstairs, next door to Wings and Things, where Mac's restaurant was. I grabbed a steak sandwich and chilled with his boys. When I was leaving, Mac showed up. He told me to follow him around the corner. I followed him to a house not far from where we were. When we arrived, Mac pulled out a very large box. We went into the house, and he opened it. As soon as he opened the box, the aroma of the chronic consumed the area we were in. All I could do was smile. JACKPOT! He gave me the seven pounds that I bought and three of his own. They were in ten-pound increments so he had to give me his. I told him that I would get rid of his before I even touched mine. I asked him for something to smoke right then because I didn't want to open the bundle until I got home. He gave me an ounce. He told me that he brought his wife back with him and that they were going to make it work. I was happy for him, and I was also happy that he had made it back safely with bomb. Mac said that he was going to spend some time with his wife and that we would hook up later and pop a couple of bottles of Cristal. He said that he had to run and meet a couple of people before he picked his wife up. I was down with the bottle popping. I told him thanks and that I loved him!

I went home and put the weed up. To kill time, I grabbed Angel and Catalina. Renee was rolling with me. We picked up her kids and headed to the movies before we even made it to the movie, I got a call from Tabby, and she was breathing hard, crying. I asked her what was wrong. She hollered that Mac had just got killed. What?! I had just left him an hour and a half ago. I was on Longview Road, and it happened on 113th Street. I was only three blocks away. I flew to the block, driving fast as hell.

When I arrived, police were all over and had taped off the scene. Renee and I jumped out of the car, leaving the kids. I tried to run into the house, but Mac's homeboy snatched me back. Renee ran into the house, and the police carried her back out. She was crying and saying she saw him. He was lying in the kitchen dead. My knees got weak. I fell to the ground, just like I'd seen people do on television when their families were killed, shit was real.

I told God to help me. I couldn't breathe. I had just been laughing and smiling with him less than two hours ago, he had just reunited with his wife and brought her back to the city, and now he was dead. My brother and my plug were gone. What was I going to do? I thought about Catalina and the blood test. I wondered who would do some shit like this, and I would soon find out.

Turk was Mac's boy. He was shot five times in the stomach and chest but made it through. They took him to St. Joseph Hospital, where my mother worked. I called her crying and told her what had happened to Mac. I told her that Turk arrived at the hospital and asked her to check on him.

Once we spoke with Turk, he told us that Mac was delivering a couple of kilos of cocaine to the cats, and they were meeting at his killer's mother's house, which was the same two niggas that I didn't trust, the same ones that he took to the Super Bowl. They probably never would have gone if it wasn't for Mac. Turk said that when they pulled up, the snake niggas were standing at the door looking strange. Mac left the drugs in the trunk, but not because they were looking strange. Mac went in to talk to them while Turk and the other homie, Pooky, stayed in the car. After five minutes or so, one of the cats came outside to the car and told them that Mac wanted them to come inside so they could smoke. When Turk walked in, Mac was in the kitchen, on his knees, begging for his life. Turk immediately grabbed the dude closest to him and started wrestling him over his gun. Mac tried to grab the gun from the scandalous, snake ass robber holding him hostage, and the cat started shooting him, while the other cat shot at Turk. Pooky jumped out of a kitchen window, and Turk managed to get through the front door. Mac was shot in the head and chest. Turk cried as he told us, and so did we. I couldn't understand how people could be so scandalous to rob and kill someone at their mother's house. I knew they were up to no good all along. Karma was a bitch, and I wanted karma to eat their hoe, SNAKE asses up!

What a sad day it was. My world was crumbling down. I didn't want the weed that I just got from Mac. I wanted Mac and needed him even more. Things couldn't get any worse. All I could do was to pray to stay sane. I started feeling like I was bad luck.

I finally got up the nerve and called Lex. I told him that I wanted to see him before I went to California for Mac's funeral. I needed a shoulder to cry on. Mac was my boy, and I was going to be there for him, dead or alive, near or far. I came upon hundreds of thousands of dollars dealing with Mac, and now he was gone. If he only would have listened, maybe he would still be alive. I had money and weed but was unhappy as ever. Who said money brings happiness? More money…more problems.

Lex came through and asked me what happened. I told him about Mac and the snakes that he was dealing with and how they killed him pretty much execution style. I told him to be careful with whatever he was doing in Kansas City because these cats would get up under him, rob or take his life. Lex said he was just chilling and not making moves. I was so tired of that lie. I didn't know who he thought he was fooling. He had drug dealer written all over his face. I didn't attract squares. Or maybe I did, and they didn't know how to step to me, but D-boys, we connected well. Lex hugged me and told me that he would be there for me and everything would be all right. I fell asleep in his arms with a broken heart.

Tabby, Renee, and I flew to California. We drove to Bakersfield, California from L.A. We stopped at Roscoe's then headed out. When we arrived, Mac's family welcomed us with open arms. I knew most of them because they had been living in the city with him. We smoked Cush the whole time we were there, rode around the city met his family, friends, barber, and everyone he loved. Mac had a beautiful home going, but it was time to get back to Killa City and face reality without him. The town was going mad. I would have to get out of the game, or I would fall victim to the streets.

Epilogue

When we arrived back home, I started dating Lex. He helped me get through my bad days. We always went out for dinner, and a movie or one of us was cooking. He drank Remy Martin VSOP or 1738, so we drank together, ate together, and had explosive, nasty sex together. The new millennium was about to begin. It was "anything goes" when it came to sex. I was grown, and Lex got for real, uncensored, nasty sex that no one else had gotten, and of course, we used a condom.

I sold all my weed and opened a boutique called Lost and Found International Fashion in Grandview with Charlie. Lex helped me get the clothes and fix up the shop. He was a big boy, two hundred and sixty pounds or more, but there wasn't one cat in Kansas or Missouri, or pretty much anywhere else, that could out dress him or match his jewels. Lost and Found was the name I chose for my new business because it was time to start a new chapter of my life and find myself.

There had been so many murders in town Richie Rich received a life sentence in federal prison. His mom received eight years. Rashad had been sentenced to life in prison. Turk and Pooky never came back to Kansas City, they didn't show up for the court, and the two snakes that killed Mac didn't receive a day. The town would never change, but I would, or die to trying.

I said that I was done selling drugs and dealing with bad boys, but was I? After all, some thunder cat more than ten years younger than I was had popped up on the scene, making grown man moves, he started inquiring about me. Besides that, now I had Lex in my life. I didn't know anything about him except his name and that he was from Texas. Was Lex his real name? The only reason I knew he was from Texas was that of his accent, and he couldn't stop saying that something was "throwed," or "already." He was most definitely from Texas. What was his purpose in Kansas City if he wasn't selling drugs? Damn, I would soon find out. The moral of the story that I learned is, if you don't walk away, there are only two ways out of the game. PRISON or DEATH!! Choose wisely.

Rest in Heaven: L.C. Dunlap, Meatball Dunlap, Delshon D, Durwin, Fontaine "Mac," Chucky J, Mary G, Jason H, Mike D, Mac Dre, Gerald Levert and so many more. Gone but NEVER be forgotten.

ABOUT THE AUTHOR

Demetria 'Mimi' Harrison is the mother of three, and grandmother to seven lovely grandchildren. Ms. Harrison has written two other books, YEARNING FOR YURI and YURI'S VENGEANCE. This book will certainly not be her last literary endeavour. She plans on delivering a wide selection of books to you for your reading pleasure. Mimi is currently a Florida resident. She engages daily in activities to grow and challenge herself. She is taking classes at Daytona State College for Business Management, as well as a publishing and writing course. She engages in anything that helps to keep her focused on her goals. With support from her family, friends, fans, and the Highest, her Father God on her side, she continues her quest to achieve literary greatness.

Each new novel, with an ever-expanding cast of characters, seeks to draw the reader in, so they feel like part of the book and become emotionally involved with the plots and players.

We are quite sure you will enjoy her true story, *She's Just Like Me* and watch for future novels.

WRITE THE AUTHOR

mimi@bossstatuspublishing.com or visit us at

www.bossstatusbublishing.com for her latest releases,

merchandise, apparel, and where to find Mimi next.

27936014R00133

Made in the USA
Columbia, SC
09 October 2018